formation service
ford, Dublin 16
13 Fax 2959479

SURVIVING STRESS

A Guide for Managers & Employees

SAMUEL A MALONE

www.oaktreepress.com

OAK TREE PRESS
19 Rutland Street, Cork, Ireland
www.oaktreepress.com

A catalogue record of this book is
available from the British Library.

ISBN 1-86076-295-6

Printed in Ireland.

CONTENTS

FIGURES

INTRODUCTION

Stress is one of the most talked-about topics of modern life. Everyday, there is some mention of it in the newspapers. It has been described as an epidemic of modern living, to which many illnesses are now attributed.

It has become almost fashionable to say that you suffer from stress. In the workplace, it is seen by some as a badge of honour, a sign of major commitment and loyalty to the firm. Some organisations have a macho approach to stress, refusing to see it as a problem in the workplace that should be addressed.

But stress has now become a cause of litigation. Many successful cases for work-related stress illnesses have been taken by employees against their employers and substantial awards have been made. Firms have finally woken up to the fact that, if they do not take a responsible approach to stress in the workplace, it may cost them a lot of money. Apart from the ethics and humanity involved, it is now proving cost-effective to have a comprehensive stress management policy in place.

In clear, non-technical language, **Surviving Stress** gives you the information, techniques, and skills necessary to tackle any stress problem you are likely to encounter in the workplace.

You are shown how to recognise the behavioural, emotional, physical and psychological symptoms of stress and how to deal with them.

You will learn how stress affects your health and what you can do to counteract it.

This book draws from a wide range of recent research and is full of practical advice and invaluable information.

It will prove invaluable to managers and those responsible for formulating strategies to combat stress in the workplace. It will also act as a source of ideas for trainers designing stress management programmes. Mnemonics, memory devices to help you recall information, are included throughout the text.

Employees who want to take a more proactive approach to stress avoidance and stress management will find plenty of ideas in **Surviving Stress** to help them achieve that end.

Sam Malone
Dublin
April 2004

1: UNDERSTANDING STRESS

- What is stress?
- What are stressors?
- What is the General Adaptation Syndrome?
- What is the arousal curve?
- What are the causes of stress?

◆

If you tighten the strings too much, they will snap, and if you leave them too slack they won't play, but if they are tuned to the right point, then and only then does the music start.
Siddhartha Gautama

MIND MAP OF CHAPTER 1

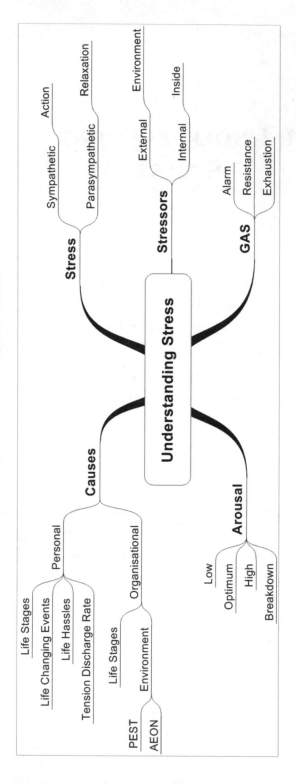

Stress is often referred to as the epidemic of the twenty-first century. It is an everyday topic of conversation. Most people will experience stress at some time in their personal or work lives. In many organisations, stress is considered a taboo subject. If acknowledged, it is often seen as a badge of honour rather than a cause of serious illness. Macho men just do not get stressed.

WHAT IS STRESS?

Medically, stress is the rate of wear and tear on the body. The body has a balancing mechanism called the autonomic nervous system, which controls the heart, lungs, stomach, blood vessels and glands. It has two elements:

- The **sympathetic** element triggers off an arousal response and prepares the body for action.
- The **parasympathetic** element restores the body to a state of relaxation.

Feelings of tension, nervousness, impatience, tiredness, anxiety, sleeplessness and various illnesses can be subjective perceptions of stress. Stress may also be considered an imbalance – real or perceived – between an individual's resources or capabilities and the demands placed upon them. Stress is often in the eye of the beholder.

The three main causes of stress are:

- Personal.
- Organisational.
- Environmental.

People experience different stress levels at different stages of their lives. Cumulative life-changing events may trigger serious stress-related illnesses. Life hassles are the everyday events that frustrate us. The tension discharge rate is our unique ability to offload stress at the end of the working day.

Many organisations are inherently stressful because of the way they are designed, organised, structured, managed and run. In fact, some organisations subject their employees to excessive workloads, control, discipline, bullying, and discrimination.

Organisations experience different stress levels at different stages of the organisational life cycle. Changes in the external environment can also be a major source of stress for organisations.

You cannot abolish stress from your life. You can only try to manage it effectively.

STRESSORS

Stressors are situations that cause stress – situations which, when compared to past events and the resources at your disposal, are perceived as threatening or challenging.

Stressors can be categorised as external and internal:

- **External** stressors come from our environment. These might include the death of a spouse, losing one's job or being criticised by another person.
- **Internal** stressors come from inside us. We create mentally the majority of our upsets including anger, sadness, fear, guilt, frustration, and shame. Unlike external stressors, internal stressors are to a large extent within our control.

The reaction to a stressor depends on the individual and the particular situation. Some people would find viewing a dead body stressful while others like police, doctors and nurses may not, as they are accustomed to seeing dead bodies in the course of their work. However, in a different context, seeing the body of a close relative or friend would get a different stress reaction.

A common example of a work stressor is work overload. This can easily be eliminated by redesign of work, delegation and time management. *Managers have a responsibility to understand stress and its causes and to take appropriate action to make the workplace as stress-free as possible.*

THE GENERAL ADAPTATION SYNDROME

A major breakthrough in our understanding of stress was the discovery of the general adaptation syndrome by Dr Hans Selye (1984). The mnemonic ARE will help you recall its stages:

- **Alarm:** The "fight or flight" response prepares the body for action. Defence mechanisms in the body become active. The body produces chemicals such as adrenaline that stimulate action in the brain, heart and muscles, helping the body to get ready to defend itself, speeding up breathing and heart rate. Blood pressure rises as blood is pumped into the muscles making them tense and ready to spring into action. Blood thickens in anticipation of repairing wounds and sugar levels increase. If the stressor is dealt with at this stage, the body will return to the normal relaxed state.

- **Resistance:** The stressor remains and the body continues to fight the stress, even though the fight or flight response has passed. High levels of the stress chemicals are still being released into the body. Personal financial problems, a job you hate, or poor health can cause chronic stress, giving rise to anxiety attacks and mood swings. If the stressor is successfully dealt with, physical signs of stress will disappear. Otherwise, the body's ability to resist the stress becomes exhausted.

- **Exhaustion:** This stage is the greatest threat to individuals. Where the body is unable to cope because it has been subjected to long-term stress, the immune system may break down, leaving the person with no defence against infections. Blood pressure, cholesterol, and blood sugar may remain high, adding the risk of a heart attack. A person who feels continually threatened will have elevated levels of the stress chemicals in their blood all the time. Prolonged overproduction of these chemicals may have detrimental effects on memory, learning and sleep.

THE AROUSAL CURVE

The arousal curve tracks the evolution of stress over time, from low stress through optimum stress to high stress and, ultimately, to breakdown. Being able to identify the stages of stress will help you to know when stress is going from bad to worse, so that timely remedial action can be taken.

There are four stages to the arousal curve:

1. **Too little stress or low stress:** In this stage, there is little challenge and no sense of personal achievement. Skills are not being used. This lack of stimulation leads to boredom and lethargy called rust-out. There is a lack of purpose, meaning or excitement in life.

2. **Optimum stress or medium stress:** In this stage, life is balanced and, despite the ups and downs of everyday living, it is perfectly manageable. A sense of job satisfaction and personal achievement enables you to get through your daily work without too many hassles. Stress in modest amounts helps you solve difficult problems and come up with creative solutions. Life is a challenge, but manageable and thoroughly enjoyable. At the end of the day, you are tired but satisfied with the way you have spent your day.

3. **Too much stress or high stress:** In this stage, you are constantly feeling you have too much to do each day. You continue to take on burdens without realising the damage that it is doing to you. Despite feeling emotionally and physically drained, you are unwilling to take time off for rest and relaxation. You are in a permanent state of anxiety and overdrive and consequently not as effective in achieving results as you should be.

4. **Breakdown:** In this stage, you may develop chronic compulsive disorders such as perfectionism or other more serious psychosomatic illnesses. You may start drinking alcohol or smoking excessively, relying on tranquillisers to help calm your nerves or sleeping pills to help you sleep. You may become more accident-prone at work or at home, as your mind becomes preoccupied with unresolved issues. You may become withdrawn or aggressive towards others. Without help or support, you are likely to have a mental or physical breakdown. Death is the ultimate way in which the body tells you to slow down, but, of course, by then it is too late.

PERSONAL CAUSES OF STRESS

The personal causes of stress can be grouped under four headings:
- Life stages.
- Life-changing events.
- Life hassles.
- The tension discharge rate.

Life stages

Developmental change such as pregnancy and birth, children growing up, mid-life crisis and growing old can all be anticipated and planned for but, nevertheless, they are stressful for many people. The biological life cycle teaches us that nobody is exempt from the hassles and life events that bring stress in their wake.

People typically go through the following life stages:
- **Adolescence:** A twilight zone between childhood and adulthood, adolescence is a time of great conflict between the need for emotional, intellectual and economic freedom, and the need to remain a child and be protected. It is a period of great uncertainty, turmoil and stress, when hormonal changes are taking place in the body, resulting in sexual and physical changes. However,

emotional development and maturity does not keep pace with the physical development and so this stage of life may be one of great confusion and stress, often expressed in the form of revolt against authority, aggression, pilfering, and alcoholism and drug dependence.

- **Early adulthood:** This is the stage when people find a job, build a career, make a home, marry and raise children – all of which may be sources of stress. During this period, many people settle down, make progress in their jobs, and are rewarded by promotion, an interesting career, and money. On the other hand, some people may not be fortunate in their choice of job, mate or economic circumstances. This may cause frustration, disappointment and resentment and result in much greater stress.

- **Midlife:** Between the ages of 35 and 45, people may suddenly realise that half their lives are over while some of their aspirations have not been fulfilled. Many people find that their careers have slowed down or stopped. Lost opportunities and regrets can be very depressing. Some people may feel trapped in their existing job because, as one gets older, opportunities dry up elsewhere. Life may have lost its excitement and challenge. On the other hand, midlife can be a time of contentment and great satisfaction because of greater maturity, experience and wisdom. Those with the courage to change careers successfully in midlife to pursue lifelong ambitions are the exception rather than the rule, and are likely to have researched and planned the move many years in advance.

- **Between 45 and 55:** Midlife crisis can affect anyone and bouts of anxiety and depression are its most common symptoms. Job opportunities are fewer, and those that arise take longer to master. Old knowledge, skills and methods become obsolete, and our levels of energy begin to wane. Realising that one has reached a plateau in one's career can be very disturbing. Feeling trapped, under-promoted and unappreciated is frustrating at any age but may magnify in later years as opportunities in the external economy also dry up, particularly for people over 45. The problem of ageism, fear of redundancy, obsolescence, or early retirement may add to stress at work. On the home front, marriage and family may have proved to be a disappointment. Some people may take drastic action such as starting a new relationship, changing their job, beginning to drink or gamble heavily or adopting a bizarre lifestyle. This is a dangerous time and many managers suffer heart attacks or other health problems. Those who survive often experience a stark reminder of human mortality through the deaths of close work colleagues, friends and relatives during this time – this brings its own share of stress. For some women, the menopause can be a very distressing period.

- **Getting old: 60 and over:** This is the stage when people begin to realise that time is running out – joints get stiff and one tires more easily. Age is no longer revered in the workplace and many executives suffer erosion of respect and status before they finally retire – demotion or sidelining are common experiences for many people. On the homefront, people may fear illness and dependency on others for everyday tasks. The deaths of close friends and relatives again remind one of the prospect and certainty of death. Retirement itself can be a stressful event for some – an unstructured day with little to do can provide pressures for those who are not prepared. But, for others who have lived a balanced life, with many interests and friends, retirement can prove to be a liberating experience.

Life-changing events

Life-changing events include such events as death of a spouse, divorce or losing one's job. The effects of major events happening over a short period of time are cumulative and the resultant stress may trigger off serious illness.

Holmes and Rahe (1967) devised a weighting system (**Figure 1**), reflecting the relative severity of each event. If a person experiences the equivalent of more than 150 points in one year, there is a 50% or more chance of that person becoming ill during the following year. The chance of illness increases to 80% for scores exceeding 300.

Figure 1 also highlights the fact that stress is a normal aspect of living.

FIGURE 1: THE HOLMES-RAHE TOP 10 LIFE EVENTS

Rank	Life Event	Value
1	Death of a spouse	100
2	Divorce	73
3	Marriage separation	65
4	Jail term	63
5	Death of family member	63
6	Personal injury or illness	53
7	Marriage	50
8	Fired at work	47
9	Marriage reconciliation	45
10	Retirement	45

Life hassles

These are the irritating, frustrating and niggling events that happen on a daily basis – losing one's car keys, computer crashes, tight deadlines, late running trains and buses, waiting in queues, and being caught up in a traffic jam.

Life hassles also include pressures that can pile up on a person and eventually wear them down – small underlying issues that often are allowed to ferment and develop – the straw that breaks the proverbial camel's back.

In the workplace, hassles include keeping up to date with new technology, new procedures and management techniques, attending meetings, telephone calls, interruptions, interpersonal conflicts, and lack of social support at work.

People in lower socio-economic groups are exposed to more hassles, simply because they have less financial, emotional, educational and other resources to deal with the daily events of life. In particular, minority groups often suffer discrimination during their daily lives.

Hassles are counterbalanced to some extent by uplifting events but, nevertheless, on a cumulative basis they can be very stressful.

The tension discharge rate

The tension discharge rate measures the speed with which you can wind down from a stressful to a relaxed state.

Everyone experiences some degree of stress at work. However, people differ in how they deal with feelings at the end of the workday. Some leave their work-related problems behind them when they go home, where they can immediately relax and get absorbed in family activities. There is a clear delineation between work and home life. Others bring their problems home with them. They find it very difficult to forget about the job and unwind. This extra psychological baggage can be a source of stress for themselves and their families.

ORGANISATIONAL CAUSES OF STRESS

Organisational causes of stress are many and varied but include life stages and the external environment.

Life stages

Organisations, just like humans and products, go through life stages – establishment, growth, maturity and decline – each with its own stressors.

The organisational life cycle is:

- **Establishment:** This is often a period of high stress, where people are under pressure to get the organisation up and running, to breakeven and to make profits as soon as possible. This is a period of great excitement, uncertainty and risk. There is a lot to do and an awful lot to learn in a short period of time.
- **Growth:** This is also a period of high stress, though not as high as the initial stage. Growth brings its own unique problems and challenges. The increase in business activity means that there is a greater volume of work to do. The company is expanding and new structures and job positions will need to be set up. Managerial challenges increase and work overload may become a problem. Competition begins to intensify and costs may need to be strictly controlled. During this time, one needs to balance work and leisure to maintain a healthy lifestyle.
- **Maturity:** This is probably the period of least stress for an organisation. The business has been established and the pioneering work has been done. The opportunities have been exploited and the threats overcome. Cash flow is sound and profits are being made. However, competition to maintain market share may be intense. There may also be a danger of resting on one's laurels and ignoring new threats and opportunities.
- **Decline:** This is often the stage of most stress in the form of downsizing, reorganisation, merger, acquisition, or ultimately closure. The inevitable layoffs can be very stressful and traumatic

for both workers and management. Nonetheless, closure is not inevitable, as some companies adapt and survive in a niche market at a lower level of business activity.

External environment

Many aspects of the external environment can be sources of stress.

PEST is a useful mnemonic in understanding some of these sources:

- **Political:** The events of 11 September 2001, the subsequent Iraq war and the worsening Middle East situation have added to the worries and distress of many people. Consequently, the numbers of people, particularly Americans, who are prepared to travel has fallen and the airlines and tourist businesses have been adversely affected. In Ireland, the introduction of anti-smoking legislation in the workplace from 1 April 2004 has implications for pubs, restaurants and hotels.

- **Economic:** The business cycle means that the economy can be in stages of contracting, expanding or stability, each of which brings its own unique stressors. Adverse changes in interest rates and foreign exchange rates, fluctuating energy prices or changes in taxation regimes can make or break a company.

- **Social:** Social changes, such as early retirement schemes now operated by many companies, can have stress implications for those involved.

- **Technological:** Industrialisation and rapid technological growth results in the depletion of the world's natural resources and widespread pollution. Radiation from nuclear technology is a danger to human health, causing leukaemia and other cancers and genetic defects in newborn babies. Man-made chlorine- and bromine-based chemicals react with sunlight in the atmosphere to destroy the ozone layer, thus increasing the risk of skin cancer due to ultraviolet radiation from the sun. All of these can be source of great stress to those affected.

The mnemonic AEON will help you recall the other major external environmental factors that may contribute to stress:

- **Atmospheric pollution:** Pesticides are one of the most widespread sources of chemical pollution in the air, water, soil and food and are now linked as a cause of cancer. In the agricultural sector, mad cow disease can be passed through to humans through the food chain. Chemical contaminants can be ingested when eating fish and shellfish, as well as vegetables and fruit. People are also worried about the additives and preservatives put in food and about the way food is processed, handled, stored and distributed. Many food manufacturers add sugar and salt to processed food – exposing customers to the risk of diabetes, stroke and heart disease because of the over-consumption of sugar and salt in their diets.

- **Ethics:** Ethics appears to rank as a low priority in some organisations. Yet breach of ethics can have disastrous consequences for the image and long-term viability of a company. Moral or ethical dilemmas in the workplace are potentially stressful. Employees are sometimes caught in a situation where there is a clash between their own personal values and those of the company. Challenging the situation by whistle-blowing can be equally stressful, as it may result in adverse consequences for their careers or, in a worst-case scenario, in being fired.

- **Overpopulation:** Population growth, increased urbanization, overcrowding in cities, traffic congestion and pollution cause stress. Expensive accommodation costs in cities forces people to buy houses many miles outside the city and to commute from long distances, creating further sources of stress.

- **Noise pollution:** Industrial noise is not only stressful to those living in the immediate area but also to employees who may be exposed to noise in their workplaces over long periods of time. Vehicle traffic in urban areas is a major source of noise to people living in towns and cities. Generally, high noise levels create stress, resulting in feelings of annoyance, frustration, intolerance and moodiness.

SUMMARY

A simple definition of stress is the wear and tear on the body. It is an imbalance between an individual's capabilities and the demands placed upon them. Stress may vary from person to person and is often in the eye of the beholder.

Stressors are conditions that cause stress. Work overload is an example.

ARE is a mnemonic, which will help you remember the stages of the general adaptation syndrome. It stands for alarm, resistance and exhaustion. The alarm stage is the fight or flight stage; the resistance stage is where the body is actively trying to cope with the stress and restore balance; and the exhaustion stage is where the continuing and prolonged stress may cause illness.

There are four stages in the stress arousal curve, namely too little, optimum, too much and ultimate breakdown.

Personal causes of stress can be categorised as life stages, life-changing events, life hassles, and the tension discharge rate.

Organisations also go through life stages, such as establishment, growth, maturity and decline, each with its own unique stressors. Environmental stressors include political, economic, social and technical. In the modern world, the ethical environment is a significant source of stress for organisations.

2: Symptoms of Stress

- What are the symptoms of stress?
- How can the symptoms of stress be classified?
- What are the three Ps?
- What are the consequences of stress?

◆

Ulcers aren't the result of what you eat. You get ulcers from what is eating you.
Anonymous

MIND MAP OF CHAPTER 2

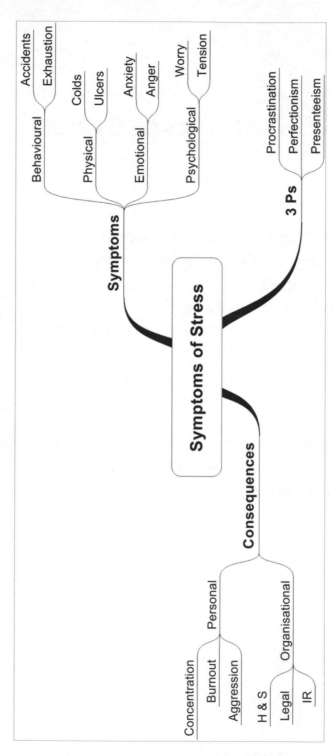

There is a current fashion to blame everything on stress. Understanding the symptoms of stress can help to deal with the consequences – both personal and organisational – that result.

SYMPTOMS OF STRESS

The symptoms of stress include behavioural, emotional, physical and psychological symptoms.

Behavioural symptoms

The behavioural symptoms of stress include:

- **Alcohol, drug abuse, and excessive smoking:** Employees may use these as coping mechanisms to escape from the monotony of a routine or stressful job. Some become addicted to alcohol, smoking and drugs – with dire health implications. *An employer may provide help to those who want to break these habits, since healthy employees are happier and more productive.*

- **Eating disorders:** Some people eat when they are stressed – "comfort eating". The problem is that comfort eating usually involves the wrong kinds of food, such as convenience foods and snacks high in sugar, salt and fat. Thus, over-eating as an escape mechanism may lead to obesity. On the other hand, under-eating may be symptomatic of anorexia nervosa, an eating disorder characterised by severe weight loss, in which an altered self-image leads sufferers to believe they are overweight when, in fact, they are dangerously underweight. It mostly affects young women and is often stress-related. *If a company runs its own canteen, it can promote healthy eating among employees.*

- **Sleep problems, such as insomnia:** The most common cause of disrupted sleep is anxiety and stress. People may ignore the fact that they are under stress during the day, but find that they suffer through disrupted sleep at night.

- **Tardiness:** Continually being late for work is known as tardiness, which may give rise to disciplinary action. *However, remedial action – flexible working arrangements or the provision of social supports – may solve the problem.*

- **Absenteeism:** Absenteeism and poor productivity may be due to drug and alcohol abuse, often a mechanism for coping with stress.

Absenteeism is a significant cost to organisations and so remedial action is usually worthwhile.

- **Withdrawal:** Unpredictable mood swings, temper tantrums, aggression or irritability are clear signs of people under stress, which may be caused by work or personal issues. *Counselling may be the answer here.*

- **Risk:** Risk-taking behaviour includes reckless driving and gambling. Gambling has a self-reinforcing cycle in that, when one gambles and loses, one then gambles again in order to recoup the losses. Some people will continue to do so until they are destitute, resulting in hardship and stress for themselves and devastation for their dependents.

- **Turnover:** A high turnover of staff may be indicative of stress in the workplace – perhaps caused by poor management styles or lack of job satisfaction. *Exit interviews may bring to light specific causes of stress that can be remedied by appropriate policies and changes in the workplace or through training and development initiatives.*

- **Accidents:** A person under stress is an accident waiting to happen. Poor working methods, inadequate training, overwork and diminished concentration due to stressful working conditions can cause accidents. *A company's accidents rate should be benchmarked against similar organisations, abnormalities investigated and remedial action taken.*

- **Exhaustion:** Exhaustion, such as feeling continually tired and irritable, may be due to lack of sleep, overwork or an advance warning of a nervous breakdown. *Doctors, nurses and others in the health care industry are among the most likely to suffer from fatigue.*

- **Suicide or attempted suicide:** People who are made redundant often contemplate suicide and some even go through with it. Their lives are so identified with their jobs, and status derived from their occupation, that they see no purpose in continuing living.

Emotional symptoms

The emotional symptoms of stress include:

- **Inability to relax:** People who are jittery and constantly living on their nerves are obviously suffering from stress. *Massage, meditation and relaxation exercises are provided by some companies to help employees relax.*

- **Job dissatisfaction:** Job dissatisfaction may be due to a lack of consultation, participation or involvement in decisions. Most people like to have an input into how they do their job – they are usually less concerned about strategic issues, unless these have implications for their own jobs.

- **Anxiety:** Anxiety is a feeling of being unable to cope with anticipated problems, although a certain amount of anxiety is normal – for example, most people experience some anxiety at the prospect of going to the dentist, preparing for a performance appraisal or for a particularly important job interview. However, the over-anxious person is inclined to view every little problem as a potential catastrophe. Common types of anxiety are agoraphobia (fear of open spaces), social phobias (fear of social situations that might cause embarrassment) and specific phobias, including fear of dogs, cats, snakes, elevators, or heights. *Systematic desensitisation or gradual acclimatisation, in the care of a professional psychologist, may be used in the treatment of anxiety.*

- **Depression:** Depression is prolonged feelings of hopelessness and helplessness triggered by pessimism, loss of self-esteem, despair, despondency, inadequacy, inability to cope and tiredness. Most people are unhappy from time to time if things do not go their way but, after a short while, they manage to bounce back again. However, depression is long-term and needs professional help.

- **Anger:** Common causes of anger at work include having an idea or proposal rejected, being generally ignored or not listened to, or receiving an unwarranted reprimand from the boss.

- **Frustration:** Frustration occurs when an individual wishes to pursue a certain course of action but is prevented from doing so. Work-related frustration is behind much misbehaviour such as aggression, hostility, and sabotage. Low tolerance for frustration is a major cause of stress and arises from beliefs that life should not be hard. In contrast, high tolerance for frustration means one accepts the reality of frustration as a natural aspect of living and thus keep it in perspective.

- **Resentment:** Seeing people being promoted ahead of oneself, or being selected for high exposure project work, are common sources of resentment especially if one considers these people less qualified, experienced, or deserving.

- **Learned helplessness:** This is a type of self-inflicted brainwashing, where a person's initiative is completely sapped because of circumstances over which they feel they have no control. They fail to exert control because of previous failures, reinforcing the belief that they will fail again.

Physical symptoms

The physical symptoms of stress include:

- **Frequent colds:** It is well-known that people under stress get colds more frequently than those less stressed. Stress weakens the immune system, leaving a person's defences weak.
- **Headaches:** Headaches are sometimes caused by tension in the face and forehead and are one of the most common symptoms of stress. They are often caused by poor ventilation and workplace noise.
- **Ulcers:** Ulcers may be brought about, or aggravated, by chronic stress.
- **Cancer:** Stress is thought to suppress the immune system and thus may encourage cancers of various types to develop.
- **Heart disease:** Research from Finland (*WebMD Medical News*, 17 October 2002) shows that work stress can double the risk of dying from heart disease. Investigators found that people who reported persistent stress due to high work demand, low job security, or few career opportunities had the same risk for fatal heart attacks as people who smoke and do not exercise. High job stress was also associated with being overweight and having high cholesterol. *Workstress.net* (Summer 2003) reports that exposure to stress in the workplace significantly increases the chances of dying from a heart attack or a stroke. Those who suffer stress for at least half of their working lives are 25% more likely to suffer a fatal heart attack and have a 50% greater chance of dying from a stroke. Manual workers are more likely to suffer heart attacks because of the high pressure experienced through overtime, night shifts and hard work for low rewards.
- **High cholesterol:** High blood cholesterol levels increase the risk of coronary heart disease and stroke. Stress is known to deposit cholesterol in the arteries. It is especially life-threatening for a person to have high cholesterol and high blood pressure at the same time.
- **Alopecia:** This is where the hair falls out in large lumps and the cause is usually due to various forms of stress – for example, the stress of surgery, prolonged illness or childbirth.
- **Irritable bowel syndrome (IBS):** It is not known what causes IBS but sustained chronic stress has been known to trigger the condition. Certainly, stress seems to aggravate the condition.

Physical responses such as ulcers and headaches may presage more serious health problems in the future. But bear in mind that these problems can be caused by factors other than stress.

Psychological symptoms

Some doctors maintain that 80% of ailments are psychosomatic, in which a physical illness such as ulcers, asthma or cancer is caused, or contributed to, by a psychological process such as stress. The mind affects the body and the body affects the mind. However, these illnesses are also caused by factors other than stress.

The psychological symptoms of stress include:

- **Boredom:** Boredom may be due to routine or repetitive work – for example, on assembly lines – with mental fatigue and loss of concentration as a consequence. Having too little work to do, or doing work below one's ability, may also result in boredom.

- **Tension:** Being promoted into an awkward situation over someone else's head is a common source of tension for the person involved. Some managers feel perpetually tensed and may find it difficult "to switch off" after work. Although it is natural to feel a bit tensed before an important interview or before making an important presentation – here the tension sharpens alertness and improves performance – constant tension is a precursor to stress.

- **Worry:** People worry about anything and everything – health, jobs, children, financial situation and promotion prospects. (One humorist maintains that worry kills more people than work because more people worry than work!) Although most worries never materialise, and so many people worry about things that will never happen, worry is an all-consuming passion that ultimately leads to stress.

- **Job insecurity:** The current recession in the EU and USA has resulted in widespread redundancies and feelings of insecurity, leading to stress, for many.

- **Cognitive dissonance:** Where two simultaneously-held attitudes or beliefs are inconsistent, or where there is a conflict between belief and behaviour, cognitive dissonance results, causing tension.

- **Alienation:** People who work on an assembly line or in large bureaucratic organisations often experience feelings of meaninglessness, powerlessness, self-estrangement and isolation. Meaninglessness means one is unable to see how one's work fits into, or contributes to, the overall objectives of the organisation.

Powerlessness means one has no influence or control over work conditions. Self-estrangement means that one's heart and soul is not consumed by one's work and one does not identify with the organisation or its products. Isolation means that the working conditions result in a person feeling physically and psychologically removed from their fellow workers, supervisor, and manager. In the case of professional staff, loyalty to their profession rather than to their employer is a sign of alienation. In general, alienated employees have feelings of low self-esteem and self-worth, caused by the lack of value and respect shown by the organisation and its managers.

THE THREE Ps

The three Ps are behaviours that can contribute to stress, namely:

- Procrastination.
- Perfectionism.
- Presenteeism.

Procrastination

Procrastination has been defined as putting off until tomorrow what you should do today, which means that something you have failed to do is eventually going to become very urgent.

Procrastination is one of the behaviours used by people who are under pressure. This displacement behaviour temporarily decreases the stress levels. However, as the deadline approaches feelings of anxiety, panic and stress are experienced at even higher levels.

When making decisions and confronted with various options, none of which is clear-cut, managers may postpone the decision as long as possible. This indecision is a major source of stress. Nature abhors a vacuum – to remain calm, one must resolve outstanding issues and problems, make unpopular decisions where necessary, complete unfinished work, and deal with unresolved conflicts. *Training in decision-making, problem solving, and time management skills should be given to those who suffer from procrastination.*

Perfectionism

Perfectionism is a type of obsessive-compulsive disorder. All-or-nothing thinking forms the basis of perfectionism. Although this attitude is good in the short-term for the company, because it has a loyal – if over-zealous – employee, it is bad for the health of the employee and their family life.

Many managers are perfectionists, which means that they think every job should be done to the highest standards and that they have an intense interest in their work. Perfectionists also find it very hard to delegate, as they believe that nobody else can do the work as good or effectively as them. Failure to delegate adds to their stress.

In the long-term, the havoc and stress caused by the perfectionist on themselves and others is bad for morale and productivity.

Presenteeism

This is the opposite of absenteeism and refers to staff who just will not go home. They are physically, but not mentally, present. They may fear their jobs are under threat due to downsizing, delayering or redundancy and so come to work earlier and stay at work later, even when there is nothing to do, because they fear for their jobs. Employees may also turn up for work, even though they are too sick to be productive. Being visible is the name of the game to protect one's job, as well as setting yourself up for promotion in the future.

Many organisations take the erroneous view that employees must demonstrate their commitment by working long hours. The "long hours" culture starts at the top where directors and senior managers work long hours themselves and sometimes expect others to do likewise. It is endemic in IT, corporate finance, management consultancy and accountancy, where jobs are often well-paid but the burnout rate is also high. The result of presenteeism is high levels of stress, anxiety, depression and poor performance. Home and family life also suffers.

THE CONSEQUENCES OF STRESS

The consequences of stress can be both/either personal or organisational.

Personal

The mnemonic CABS recalls the personal consequences of stress:

- **Concentration:** Poor concentration, memory, indecisiveness and apathy are consequences of stress and result in poor decisions or mistakes.

- **Aggression:** Road rage, thought to be a consequence of living in overcrowded urban situations and driving in congested traffic conditions, has even resulted in violence and murder. A combination of alcohol and fear of flying may trigger off air rage, leading to diversion of flights.
- **Burn-out:** Burn-out is the ultimate consequence of stress, where people are completely drained and unable to cope with the pressures of work and life. The topic of burn-out is dealt with more thoroughly in **Chapter 3**.
- **Sabotage:** This is where employees intentionally damage an organisation's property, reputation, product or service.

Organisational

The organisational consequences of stress include:

- High recruitment and training costs.
- Workmen's compensation.
- Health and safety issues.
- Legal costs for stress litigation cases taken against the organisation. (The legal aspects of stress are covered in **Chapter 6**.)
- Industrial relations problems.
- Poor customer relations resulting in lost business.
- Low productivity and job satisfaction.

SUMMARY

The symptoms of stress can be behavioural, emotional, physical and psychological. It is well to bear in mind that these symptoms also can be due to factors unrelated to stress.

Behavioural symptoms include drug and alcohol abuse. Emotional symptoms include depression and anxiety. Physical symptoms include frequent colds and headaches. Psychological symptoms include boredom and job insecurity.

The three Ps – behaviours that can contribute to stress – are procrastination, perfectionism and presenteeism.

Personal consequences of stress include poor concentration, aggression and burnout. Organisational consequences include high recruitment and training costs and low productivity.

3: TYPES OF STRESS

- What are the main types of stress?
- What is the difference between distress and eustress?
- What is burn-out?
- What is post-traumatic stress disorder?
- How does stress differ between countries?
- How does stress differ between jobs?
- How does stress differ between people?

◆

If you feel that you are indispensable, put your finger in a glass of water, withdraw it, and note the hole you have left.
Anonymous

MIND MAP OF CHAPTER 3

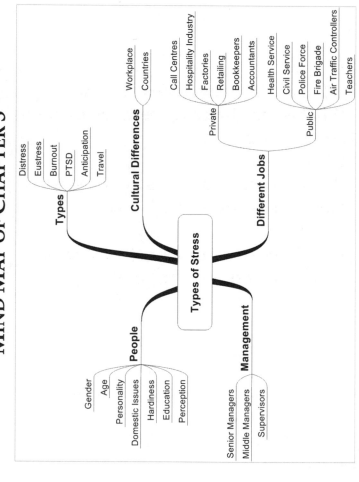

The most common types of stress are eustress, distress, burnout, and post-traumatic stress disorder. Most jobs have unique stressors attached to them. Some jobs are inherently more stressful than others, while travel stress is a feature of modern life.

Managers should be aware that different cultures bring different beliefs and attitudes to the workplace. Some jobs are more inherently stressful than others. Depending on their age, gender, and personality, people will experience stress differently. Perception determines how severe the stress reaction will be.

TYPES OF STRESS

There are many types of stress, which are considered below.

Good and bad stress

Eustress is good stress and makes life enjoyable and interesting. You feel confident, in control and able to handle the challenges and demands of life.

A sense of responsibility and challenge enhances mental sharpness, physical strength, productivity and morale. A certain amount of stress is good for people, as it motivates a person to learn new skills and overcome obstacles.

The total elimination of stress is impossible and, in any event, would greatly diminish the quality of one's life. People working on high quality assignments and to strict deadlines can often achieve remarkable results. Without the stress and challenge of deadlines, they would be unable to finish projects on time. Some work-related stress is necessary to stimulate personal growth and development and enhance professional performance.

Distress is bad stress, and is often viewed as a disease needing treatment. Distress may be due to the extra pressure caused by the excessive and unrelenting demands on one's time or personal resources. Some of the demands that can lead to distress include:

- Having too much to do.
- Promotion beyond one's level of competence.
- Being required to do tasks for which one is inadequately trained.
- Losing one's job.
- Having insufficient income to make ends meet.

In the workplace, interpersonal conflicts may be a major source of stress. Having too little to do, which is frequently the case when people retire, may also cause distress.

External and internal stress

Stress can also be categorised as external or internal.

External stressors include relatives getting sick or dying, being made redundant, or being on the receiving end of somebody's anger. On the other hand, internal stress such as anxiety and resentment comes from within and is self-generated. Since people create the majority of their own upsets and, thus cause much of their own stress, it means that stress is, to a large extent, within their own control.

Burn-out and rust-out

Burn-out is a state of physical, emotional and mental exhaustion, caused by prolonged involvement in work that is too intellectually and emotionally demanding. The converse is rust-out, caused by too little stress. According to the Yerkes Dodson Law, too little pressure is just as bad as too much pressure.

The results of burn-out may be feelings of fatigue, frustration, panic, helplessness, hopelessness, depersonalisation, loss of confidence, low self-esteem, and reduced personal accomplishment.

Depersonalisation occurs when employees start treating customers or other employees as objects rather than human beings having distinct personalities and needs. Reduced personal accomplishment is a feeling that one's achievements are of little consequence and that one's career is meaningless. For example, the person may complain of being emotionally drained, show a lack of humour, and skip rest breaks. Burn-out is most closely associated with the so-called helping professions who, on a day-to-day basis, interact extensively with others. These include nursing, teaching, social work, salespeople, police officers, customer service departments, and the hospitality industry.

Burn-out may result in substantial costs for an organisation due to high staff turnover, absenteeism, and reduced productivity.

Stages of burn-out

The stages of burn-out are:

1. **Contentment:** This is the early stage where people are happy with the job that they are doing. However, they keep putting in more

and more time and effort into the job without taking sufficient rest and recreation. As a result, they quickly arrive at the second stage.

2. **Energy deficit:** The person begins to feel tired all the time and cannot sleep soundly at night. Lack of sleep further erodes the energy bank and sets up a vicious cycle. They become cynical and complain that they have not as much energy as before. Procrastination, inability to make decisions and loss of creativity are common problems.

3. **Stage of chronic symptoms:** Feeling tired and exhausted characterises this stage. A once calm person is now continually on edge and ready to explode.

4. **Crisis:** The person becomes obsessed with the job. They become so preoccupied with the job that they can think of, and talk about, nothing else. They work long hours, bring work home at weekends, and are reluctant to go on holidays.

5. **Breakdown:** The person may feel overwhelmed by it all and may drown themselves in alcohol and drugs. Others may have a mental or physical breakdown, such as severe depression or a heart attack.

Managers should recognise the stages of burnout in themselves, and in their staff, so that preventative action can be taken.

Post-traumatic stress disorder

Post-traumatic stress disorder (PTSD) has been defined as specific psychological symptoms that occur after a person experiences a severe and traumatic event. Symptoms, which persist for at least one month, include a state of increased arousal, avoidance or emotional numbness, and constant flashbacks of the traumatic event.

Originally applied to American veterans of the Vietnam War, the term is sometimes regarded as a modern synonym for shell-shock or battle-fatigue. In the early part of the 20th century, the condition of soldiers in war situations who found themselves unable to cope because of the incessant bombing, killing, depersonalisation, lack of respect for human life, and autocratic leadership style, was little understood and many were treated as cowards.

In everyday life, those who have suffered serious accidents, witnessed traumatic events, experienced child physical or sexual abuse may suffer PTSD. In some jobs, such as the police and ambulance service, where people can be constantly exposed to natural disasters, terrorist attacks, fires, road accidents, murders and assaults, they may experience PTSD. Victims of street violence may experience anxiety, depression, phobias, and post-traumatic stress disorder. In organisations, employees might experience PTSD, if they go through the ordeal of being caught up in an armed robbery or witness a serious accident at work.

Research indicates that 25% of those who experience PTSD suffer long-term effects. In addition, it has been found that physical changes occur in the brain as a result of PTSD. The hippocampus, a structure that lies deep in the brain and is linked with memory, is smaller in PTSD victims. *Counselling services should be provided as a matter of course for those suffering from PTSD.*

Anticipatory stress

Thinking about a stressful situation is enough to trigger stress for some people.

The human imagination is inclined to run riot, if not reined in and calmed down. Just think about the last time you were asked to make a presentation. What thoughts and pictures went through your mind? Public ridicule is a common image, with people laughing at you, getting bored or walking out. Other people worry about the possibility of being asked difficult questions that they may be unable to answer. These potentially difficult situations should be perceived as challenges rather than threats.

Just as one can anticipate stress, one can also use appropriate strategies such as planning, preparation, and goal-setting to deal with likely scenarios. These strategies can be rehearsed in one's mind and positive responses and outcomes imagined. Picture the audience being very receptive and welcoming, anticipate the warm reception to the presentation, hear the loud applause and glow with a feeling of pride, admiration and satisfaction – and thus remove anticipatory stress.

Travel stress

People who travel abroad a lot on business may experience jet lag, caused by the disruption of the 24-hour circadian cycle of night and day. This is a recognised stressor, affecting the application of skills and the exercise of managerial judgement. Travellers crossing time zones rapidly experience problems similar to those of shift workers such as disturbed sleep and increased fatigue. In addition, marriages and families may suffer if managers spend a lot of their time away from home. Airlines recognise jet lag as a source of stress for staff.

People who commute to work from suburbia often experience delays due to traffic congestion and road works. In addition to the time and expense of commuting, commuters face the daily hassle of traffic jams, accidents, rude and aggressive drivers and competition for parking spaces. Commuting time can now add 30% or more to a person's working week. *This type of stress can often be avoided by planning journeys or working flexible hours to avoid peak times.*

A displacement strategy, especially useful for those studying part-time, when stuck in traffic is to listen to educational or self-development tapes instead of fuming. In the case of car travel, managers with good time management skills are less prone to accidents, because they are more likely to plan and allow extra time for their journeys. They are thus less likely to get stressed or indulge in dangerous driving to get to their destinations on time.

Seasonal affective disorder

SAD is a form of depression, in which moods change with the seasons. Sufferers tend to feel depressed in winter and feel better in spring. More people commit suicide in December, when the days are shortest and the nights are longest, than in any other month of the year.

Bright sunny days cheer people up, while dark cloudy days have the opposite effect. Lack of sufficient sunlight creates an imbalance of certain chemicals in the brain. Exposure to bright light for two to four hours a day can relieve depression in some people. *So do yourself a favour and get out in the daylight for a few hours each day. The exercise and fresh air will also stimulate your brain and improve your concentration.*

CULTURAL DIFFERENCES

Western organisations should be aware of cultural differences in work values, attitudes, dress code and religion, together with potential communication problems caused by people not being proficient in English. Managers may need training to raise their awareness of the issues involved. Employees from minority ethnic groups may be prone to additional sources of stress caused by racism, stereotyping, discrimination and language difficulties.

People in different countries have different attitudes towards work. Although the British work the longest hours in the EU, generally Westerners have adopted the Protestant work ethic, which takes the view that work is inherently good and salvation in the next life can be earned by hard work in this life. The Japanese also have a reputation for working very long hours. The stress induced by this overwork reaches such intense levels that it results in sudden death, a syndrome known as *karoshi*.

Other differences are that Western cultures focus more on the individual and competition, while Eastern cultures focus more on the group and collaboration. Western ideas of equality do not translate easily into other cultures. For example, in some Arab cultures it is not acceptable for men to report to women. The Chinese tradition of secrecy about business affairs, coupled with politeness and avoidance of open argument, is very different from the American style of transparency and confrontation. One culture may interpret body language differently from another, causing all kinds of misunderstandings.

DIFFERENT JOBS

Some jobs are inherently more stressful than others. It is well known that air traffic controllers and nurses have particularly stressful jobs. At the other extreme, bookkeepers experience little stress in their jobs, although accountants experience high stress levels as tax deadlines approach.

Generally, jobs dealing with people are more stressful than jobs dealing with things such as buildings or equipment. Similarly, jobs with a high level of responsibility are more stressful than jobs with little or no levels of responsibility.

In the final analysis, a person's perception of their role will determine whether they experience stress or not. Different individuals will react differently to the same work situation, one finding it enjoyable and rewarding, another finding it quite stressful.

Private Sector

- **Call centres:** These seem to be the modern equivalent of sweatshops, where the principles of scientific management have been applied to jobs to demand greater efficiency with maximum management control and minimum employee discretion. Criteria such as average call-handling time, and number of calls taken in a specified period, are used to measure performance. Close supervision, time pressures, constant performance monitoring, and the associated lack of control and trust, make these potentially stressful jobs. Some UK call centres, in a quest for greater cost efficiency, have relocated to low-cost economies, like India. The resulting job insecurity has further added to the stress of call centre employees. Call centres tend to have a high rate of staff turnover, with boredom and lack of job satisfaction the usual reason given for leaving.

- **Hospitality industry:** People in the hospitality industry often work long hours and are sometimes poorly paid. There is a high rate of interaction with customers, although lack of training in customer contact skills often adds to the stress and difficulties of the job. Their work has seasonal variations and peaks and troughs on a daily basis. Kitchen staff have no contact with customers and so a vital cue for direct feedback and job satisfaction is missing. Managerial styles tend to be autocratic which doesn't help industrial relations problems.

- **Factories:** Work on an assembly line is routine and monotonous. There is poor person-environment fit and low participation and use of abilities. Noise is often a constant irritant. Employees are more likely to experience rust-out than burn-out. Feelings of alienation, meaninglessness, self-estrangement and isolation are common. Employees on an assembly line find it difficult to communicate and interact with each other and therefore feel socially isolated. Machine-paced work has been linked to anxiety, anger and depression but only for Type A workers (see **Chapter 5**).

- **Retailing:** Face-to-face contact with difficult customers can be stressful. The customers themselves may be suffering from stress. For example, in the airline industry, one may be dealing with a customer whose luggage has been mislaid. In a shop, one may be dealing with a customer returning defective goods. *Such situations can be resolved successfully by fair policies and good customer contact skills.*

Public Sector

- **Health Service:** Professions such as emergency medical technicians, general practitioners, consultants, junior hospital doctors, and nurses are particularly stressful. Nursing terminally ill patients, those in considerable pain such as cancer patients, and those in intensive care units can be particularly stressful. Jinks and Daniels (1999) report that the work of nurses makes them prone to stress-related illnesses. Nurses are particularly prone to burn-out – high workloads, budgetary constraints, bureaucratic controls, and staff shortages are identified as major sources of

psychological stress in nurses. Similarly, doctors in junior to
senior grades were reported to suffer from psychological distress
such as anxiety, emotional exhaustion, clinical depression and
even suicide, due to long hours and heavy workloads. It is well
known that medical doctors have the highest suicide, drug
addiction, and divorce rate of any profession. Earnshaw &
Morrison (2001) report that social workers, by the nature of their
work, face harrowing jobs in local government. They have seen
nearly 20 years of budgetary cut after cut; all have caseloads that
are sky-high; many are dealing with extremely difficult situations
often without adequate training, supervision or support. Limited
resources, with a heavy and difficult caseload, make this a most
stressful job.

- **Civil Service:** Stress is prevalent in the Civil Service. Five main
  reasons are often cited: bureaucracy, understaffing, change, tight
  budgets, and a lack of training. Civil Service departments are
  trying to move away from a bureaucratic management style and
  adopting a more commercial and cost conscious approach to
  business. In the process, staff find themselves under constant
  pressure, as modern management techniques are introduced and
  implemented.

- **Police force:** Certain stressors are expected to be associated with
  police and prison-work. For example, dangerous assignments can
  be a source of considerable distress. Other stressors may include
  tension, mental fatigue, abuse, hostility and violence from some
  segments of the public, and sometimes, extreme monotony. The
  bureaucracy in which the police work may cause stress. Lack of
  management support, autocratic leadership styles, poor
  promotion prospects, inadequate training and equipment,
  excessive paperwork, and frustration with the criminal justice
  system including court leniency, are just some of the reasons
  police officers experience stress.

- **Fire brigade:** This is a dangerous and inherently stressful job. Fire
  kills and maims and the fire brigade is in the front-line, putting
  their personal safety at risk. Like the police force, they are often
  subject to abuse, hostility and violence from some segments of the
  public.

- **Air traffic controllers:** Air traffic controllers (ATCs) experience
  considerable stress, especially during busy periods. They have
  responsibility for the lives of others and need to concentrate
  continuously on their task, since a mistake or lapse of

concentration may have dire consequences in terms of loss of human life. Peptic ulcers, hypertension and heart disease are particularly common among ATCs.

- **Teachers:** Teaching is now considered one of the most stressful of occupations. Teachers are reaping some of the side-effects of the breakdown in discipline in society in general. Corporal punishment has been outlawed, so teachers must rely solely on persuasion to deal with ill-disciplined pupils. In addition, workload, lack of student interest, overcrowded classrooms, poor resourcing of buildings and equipment, lack of career opportunities, feelings of isolation, diminished status, and public criticism of teachers and their work has all added to the stress involved in teaching. Many teachers are voting with their feet and moving out of the profession. Of those who remain, there is a high rate of absenteeism, and early retirement due to ill health.

Management

As a general rule, the higher the management level, the more control the manager has and the less stress they experience.

At top management level, technical skills are less important. Nonetheless, balancing the demands of shareholders, board members, senior managers, investment analysts, employees, customers, government, trade unions, the media, and community organisations may be extremely stressful and requires considerable social skills.

At the very top, the isolated life experienced by the chief executive can be a further source of stress. At this level, one has no peers and is unlikely to have a confidant with whom to share personal problems or concerns.

The lower the management level, the less control managers have and the more stress they experience. Technical skills are more important at this level, but social skills are still important. Middle managers often feel they have little power and may feel vulnerable to early retirement or redundancy. Supervisors experience particular stress, because the demands from above are often irreconcilable with the expectations coming below.

Managerial jobs are becoming more demanding and complex. Delayering means more work being done by fewer people, and spans of control have increased. The volume of information that managers have to handle has increased enormously. Liston-Smith (2001) reports an international survey of managers which shows that the average manager deals with 190 messages daily and is interrupted once every 10 minutes. The result is often a state of mental and physical exhaustion known as information fatigue syndrome.

Keeping up with technology has become a major source of stress for managers. The easy accessibility and use of technology has added to, rather than reduced, the workload of managers. Greater responsibilities and longer working hours has become a feature of management jobs. The problem of achieving a healthy balance between work and home life has become a major issue for most managers. In dual career couples, where the burden of domestic work often falls primarily on the female, the health risks from working long hours may be increased for female managers.

PEOPLE

People feel stress in different ways and for different reasons.

Gender

Men feel things physically. Women feel things emotionally. Females use social support strategies more frequently than males as coping mechanisms for handling stress. Women are more likely to talk about their problems and seek assistance than men. Women confide more intimately and create deep friendships with other women, whereas men are reluctant to do so with other men.

Younger *versus* older people

Generally, older people have developed the wisdom and maturity to handle stress. Experience is said to be a great teacher, but can also be a great stress-reducer. With the passage of time, many people develop greater self-understanding and coping mechanisms to deal with the unique stressors of their organisation. They have faced similar situations before and coped successfully. On the other hand, younger people are less confident in dealing with life stressors, since they have no prior experience of dealing with them. However, there are unique stressors relevant to younger and older people such as adolescence and the mid-life crisis.

An individual's interpretation of a threat is often determined by age. A young person may see a proposed merger in the company where he works as an opportunity, while an older person may see it as a threat and therefore much more stressful.

In general, younger people are less prone to illness than older people and to the stresses and insecurities that invariably accompany illness.

Personality

Different people have different personalities and coping styles. Assumption, beliefs and expectation affect the way that a person perceives stress. Some people see things positively, while others see everything in a negative light. Some people are natural risk-takers, while others are risk-averse. High-risk individuals tend to seek out occupations to test themselves in stressful environments and avoid jobs where they would not get the opportunities to do so. Risk-averse people would find any risk taking very stressful. Risk-takers love the flow of adrenaline that accompanies the uncertainty.

Some people might be unsuited for a particular type of work. For example, they might find it difficult to manage certain work-based stressors, making decision-making in such circumstances very difficult. Some people have abrasive personalities with no interpersonal relationship skills and thus cause stress by ignoring the feelings and sensibilities of others. This suggests that aptitude and psychometric tests should be used to match the right people to the right jobs.

Workstress.net (January 2001) reports evidence to suggest that certain personality types are more accident-prone than others. Research by a team from the University of Manchester Institute of Science and Technology (UMIST) suggests three key personality traits:

1. **Dependability:** The tendency to be conscientious and socially responsible.
2. **Agreeableness:** The tendency not to be aggressive or self-centred.
3. **Openness:** The tendency to learn from experience and to be open to suggestion from others.

Personalities with low levels of the first two traits are more likely to be involved in accidents. High levels of openness are also linked to increased risk, since they tend to be somewhat dreamy and to let their imagination get the better of them. Professor Ivan Robertson of UMIST said people with low levels of agreeableness tended to be highly competitive and less likely to comply with instructions. The research has implications for the screening of people applying for potentially risky jobs, such as train drivers and air traffic controllers.

Domestic circumstances

People do bring their problems to work. Personal problems do interfere with work, especially when working under stressful conditions. It is difficult to concentrate on the task at hand, if you have unresolved personal and domestic issues. *Hence the need for counselling services, social support services, and family friendly policies such as flexible working and crèche facilities.*

Hardiness

People with the quality of hardiness are less susceptible to stress. There are observable differences between people when confronted with stress: some go to pieces at the slightest reason, while others (the "hardy" ones) are unflappable in the face of extremely provocative and stressful situations.

Hardy individuals are self-confident, with a clear sense of personal values and goals, and are not deterred by obstacles and setbacks. They have a high tolerance for frustration and discomfort and are able to cope effectively with the ups and downs of life without getting unduly distressed. They do not blow things out of proportion and are able to put things in perspective. They have a high level of commitment and involvement in what they are doing, an internal locus of control or a belief that they can influence important events in their lives, and view change not as a threat but as an opportunity to grow.

Darwin's theory of evolution suggests that the hardy people survive and the best get to the top. However, these are people who do not succumb to stress-related illnesses and are unlikely to understand or empathise with those who do.

Education

Generally, the more educated a person, the greater insight they have on business and the more they feel in control of their lives and the less stress they experience. Greater knowledge gives an understanding of life, how the world works, and confidence to deal with the issues it throws up. On the other hand, highly qualified people with low job status are likely to experience a high degree of frustration, since they need work of a high standard to match their educational attainments.

Perceptions

People differ as regard education, experience, conditioning, genes, health and personality. One person's stressful situation is another's challenge. Some people are more resilient than others, and take the normal stresses of life in their stride.

When exposed to the same situation, some people experience a high degree of stress, while others experience little or none. Take a group of people who retire at 65: some will feel severely depressed; others will feel moderately sad and frustrated and still others will feel content or happy. Obviously the same stressor (retirement) is experienced quite differently by the three groups.

Events are neutral. It is the way a person perceives the event that makes the difference. Events do not make a person angry. It is the person's perception of the events that make them angry. Becoming angry is their own decision. So the internal stress a person experiences in their life is completely within their own control.

The degree of stress will be influenced by one's perception of one's own ability, and the range of psychological, personal and physical resources at one's command to meet the particular demands of the situation:

- A person's ability to cope will be influenced by psychological factors such as interests, values, needs, self-belief and self-esteem.
- Personal resources include health, experience, expertise, and education.
- Physical resources include finance, equipment and people such as friends, relatives, work colleagues and other professionals.

A deficit in any of these resources may result in the individual being overwhelmed by a situation.

SUMMARY

The types of stress include eustress, distress, burn-out and post-traumatic stress disorder. Anticipatory stress is where people get anxious about a future event. Air and car travel are common sources of modern day stress.

People from different countries perceive stress differently, due to cultural factors.

Generally, there are different levels of stress associated with different jobs and different professions. For example, air traffic controllers have high stress jobs, while bookkeepers have jobs with little stress. In management, stress is correlated to status, with senior managers experiencing less stress than middle managers and supervisors.

People experience different levels of stress, depending on gender, age, education, personality, domestic circumstances and hardiness. Hardy people are less susceptible to stress.

Stress is often in the eye of the beholder, where perception and interpretation of a situation may play a major role in how the stress will be experienced.

4: STRESS IN ORGANISATIONS

- What are role stressors?
- What stressors are due to the work environment?
- How do strategy, structure and style contribute to stress?
- What are interpersonal relationship stressors?
- How do tasks create stress?
- What is the cost of stress?

◆

Many… have reached the top of the success ladder, but are beginning to suspect it may be leaning against the wrong wall.
Sam Keen

MIND MAP OF CHAPTER 4

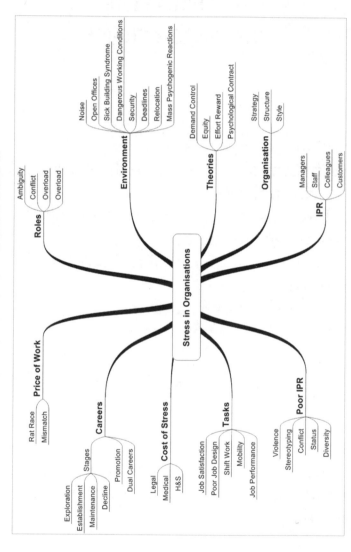

A mnemonic that will help you recall the major organisational stressors is RESIT, which stands for:

- **Role:** Role ambiguity and role conflict, role over-load and role under-load.
- **Environment:** Environmental stressors include noise and dangerous working conditions.
- **Strategy**, Structure and Style.
- **Interpersonal** relationships.
- **Task:** Including job design and job performance.

The cost of stress is now significant for most organisations. Promotion, demotion, and frustrated ambitions are stressors that many employees experience from time to time.

Managers are considered to have a career rather than a mere job. The time, energy and commitment required to keep a career on target can generate its own share of stress. Dual career families have a difficult time balancing the demands of work and family life.

ROLES THAT PEOPLE PLAY

The roles that people play include role ambiguity, role conflict, role over-load and role under-load.

Role ambiguity

This refers to a lack of clarity about how to perform one's job. It may include uncertainty about goals, how best to achieve them and how performance is evaluated.

Ambiguity may be due to inadequate training, poor communication, or the deliberate withholding or distortion of information. For lower level jobs, a job description can often solve the problem or, alternatively, an explanation about the role or on-the-job training by the manager to the employee about what the job entails. However, for managerial jobs, the removal of role ambiguity can be more difficult because of a lack of well-defined and specific routines to be carried out. This is particularly so in management jobs requiring a lot of abstract thinking, discretion, and non-programmed decision-making.

Role ambiguity differs between different functions, with human resource and sales managers reporting the most ambiguity and production and finance managers reporting the least. HRM managers often do not know the consequences of their decisions because of delayed feedback, while production and finance managers operate within defined procedures, have measurable targets, and more immediate concrete feedback.

The level of stress caused by role ambiguity varies from one person to another. Some people demand a lot of structure in their lives, while others tolerate, or even thrive on, ambiguity. Structure is found in the civil service and multinationals, while lack of structure is experienced in start-up businesses.

Generally, prolonged periods of ambiguity lead to feelings of futility, anxiety, poor job performance, low motivation, job dissatisfaction and an intention to leave the job.

Role conflict

Role conflict occurs when an employee experiences conflicting demands from different sources, where compliance with one makes it difficult to comply with the other. The person may also feel the demand is beyond the scope of their job specification. There may be conflict between an employee's values and sense of ethics and that of the company's culture. There may be conflict between the employer's expectations and those of the employee's family.

Most people perform several roles in their lives and, as a result, often find that the demands of one role conflict with another. Professional women often experience conflict between their role as a mother and that of a company executive. A shop steward may experience conflict between his role as an employee and a union representative. A supervisor is often put in a "no win" situation, having to deal with the conflicting expectations of managers and workers simultaneously.

It has been found that introverts react more negatively to role conflict than extroverts; they experience more tension and poorer interpersonal relations. In addition, studies have shown that anxious people are more likely to suffer from role conflict than people with a more calm and flexible approach to life.

WORK – TOO MUCH OR TOO LITTLE?

Having Too Much to Do

Having too much to do – work over-load – may be quantitative or qualitative.

Over-load quantitative

Situations where employees are asked to do more work in a specified period of time than they can reasonably handle may be stressful for them. Contributory factors include long hours, time pressures, deadlines, autocratic leadership, unreasonable quotas, travel, noise and frequent interruptions.

For many managers, work over-load may be self-imposed. Lack of assertiveness skills such as the inability to say 'No', poor time management skills, or failure to delegate can worsen the situation. Many managers take work home with them, and work in the evenings and at weekends. In addition, many managers read journals at home to keep up-to-date, because they find it impossible to concentrate at work, due to constant interruptions, phone calls, and noise. These practices have become the norm in many organisations and managers feel they have to adhere to them, as otherwise their commitment and loyalty would be questioned and their promotional chances diminished.

Working women are particularly prone to over-load. In a man's world, they often feel they have to work harder and longer than their male colleagues do in order to maintain visibility, get recognition, show their commitment, and improve their chances of being promoted. In addition, on the domestic front, they often do more than their fair share of the work, since the vast majority of men are still reluctant to do housework.

Over-load qualitative

Work perceived as being too difficult – where a person feels they lack the requisite education, technical competencies or training to do the job satisfactorily – can be stressful. For example, a person may be asked to perform tasks for which they have received no training, or may be promoted beyond their level of competence.

Having too little to do

Just as having too much to do may be stressful, counter-intuitively having too little may be equally stressful. Under-load also may be quantitative or qualitative.

Under-load quantitative

This means having an insufficient quantity of work to do. Under-load can lead to boredom and monotony that, in turn, can lead to stress. Doing nothing can be as stressful as doing too much.

However, the degree of job dissatisfaction caused by work under-load differs from one occupation to another. It seems to have little effect on the job dissatisfaction of assembly-line workers and policemen but increases job dissatisfaction for administrators.

Under-load qualitative

This is where the work is of an insufficient quality to hold one's interest and the lack of mental stimulation may become a source of stress. This is often a feature of routine and repetitive jobs, where the work may be devoid of problem-solving, creativity, new challenges or social interaction. The outcome may be poor job satisfaction and high absenteeism. For example, teachers follow the same syllabus year after year, accountants produce the same information month after month, lorry drivers drive the same routes and experience the same frustrations over and over again. People need variety, new challenges and opportunities to learn new skills through training and development.

But note that many interesting jobs have also periods of qualitative under-load, since few jobs provide mental stimulation and challenge all the time. There is no harm in this, as people need time to mentally recuperate and reflect. The Pareto Principle seems to operate in this regard, in that 20% of the work will provide most of the interest, mental stimulation and challenge, with the balance being mostly routine.

Hard work never killed anybody

People who are committed and enjoy their work seem to be able to work long hours without any adverse health problems. Many executives work 60-hour weeks with no apparent ill effects. The problem seems to be work that is routine, monotonous, unsatisfying and frustrating.

In the Western world, the Protestant work ethic, which proclaims the virtues of hard work, thrift and competition – reigns supreme. There is nothing wrong with the Protestant work ethic – however, the extreme application of the concept encourages work addiction and leads to burn-out.

ENVIRONMENTAL STRESSORS

There are numerous environmental stressors in the workplace damaging to employee health. The better-known stressors are:

- **Noise:** We are born with an inherent fear of loud noises, which can trigger the stress response, since they suggest something harmful in our environment, raising blood pressure and accelerating the heartbeat. Unpredictable noise is particularly stressful. *A simple way to counteract the effects of noise is to wear earplugs. For certain jobs, under health and safety legislation, ear defenders are obligatory.*

- **Open offices:** Most employees are not given the opportunity to influence the design of their offices. Private offices are still the norm for executive staff, while clerical and administrative staff work in an open-plan environment. Some people have no problems with working in open offices while others find the experience stressful because of the noise and interruptions. Once more, stress is often in the eye of the beholder.

- **Sick building syndrome:** The cause of sick building syndrome is said to be poor air quality related to inadequate ventilation, low humidity, high levels of airborne dust and poor temperature control. When it is present, more people than usual suffer from headaches, sore eyes and throats, dry mouth and poor concentration, and begin to complain of feeling unwell. Symptoms increase in severity in direct proportion to the time spent in a particular building. Most notorious are the rare cases of Legionnaire's Disease, which is caused by a bacterium breeding on pools of water in ventilation ducts. In some cases, sick building syndrome can be traced to chemicals in carpeting adhesives, pulsating fluorescent lights and computer screen glare.

- **Dangerous working conditions:** Dangerous conditions including toxic chemicals, radiation, unsafe work practices, crowded work areas and long hours. Many industrial processes produce harmful substances that pollute the air and enter the human body through the mouth, nose, lungs and skin. Exposure over long periods of time may cause serious illnesses, including cancer, leukaemia and genetic defects.

- **Security:** In the past, having the same job for up to 45 years was not unusual. For some, promotion offered some challenge and variation but with the same degree of security. In the modern work world, there are now no jobs for life. The only certainty is uncertainty. Most people can expect to change jobs or careers many times in a lifetime. Companies come and go. They downsize, reorganise, and restructure to meet competition. People are now offered temporary employment, part-time work, and fixed term contracts renewable at the discretion of the employer. This lack of security is a major source of stress.

- **Deadlines:** Constant deadlines can be a major source of stress. People are anxious when they have a lot to do before a deadline; as the deadline approaches, feelings of impending disaster increase. The eustress of occasional deadlines is good for performance. However, if failure to meet a deadline means losing a valuable contract, or our jobs, then it can be extremely stressful.

- **Relocation, transfers, promotion and finding work:** Relocation and moving house can be stressful for both the manager and the family. Transfers may be between departments, between different location or even overseas. A transfer overseas can be particularly stressful as the person may be faced with a new culture, business practices, and language. In the short-term, promotion can cause an increase in work demands and pressure, because of the unfamiliarity of the job and new learning involved. In addition, the added responsibility can be a source of stress. *When taking over a new job make sure that you are briefed adequately by the previous incumbent. Moreover, it is only fair that you brief your successor before you leave your old job.*

- **Mass psychogenic reactions:** This is like a disease where the stress is contagious. The stress experienced by one person is spread to others in the group, so that the whole group is affected. For example, the stress experienced by a manager is often transmitted to his staff – some managers seem to create stress for others rather than for themselves. Those on the receiving end may pass on the stress, like a virus, to others in turn. Similarly, stressed managers often bring their stress home with them to their families.

THEORIES & MODELS

The demand control model, equity theory, the effort/reward imbalance theory, and the psychological contract are four useful concepts to help you understand some of the conditions generating stress in the workplace. The mnemonic DEEP can be used for recall.

Demand control model

This is where high work demands and low job control co-exist. People with high work demands often complain that they work too hard and have insufficient time to get the job done. People with low job control complain that they lack the authority to make decisions about their jobs. They work constantly under psychological pressure to externally-imposed deadlines: either may trigger off feelings of helplessness and lead to stress. People who are consulted about, and have a say in, how they work show improved levels of job satisfaction, commitment, performance and motivation and consequently suffer less stress.

High levels of control have positive health and work-related outcomes such as decreased anxiety, depression and absenteeism. Senior managers tend to have more control over their work than middle managers and supervisors, and thus are less exposed to this particular stressor. Middle managers tend to be caught in the middle, having to deal with pressure from above and below. Supervisors have a particularly difficult job, trying to balance the needs of their manager with those of their employees.

Blue collar workers are at greater risk to the affects of stress because they have little control over the work they do. On the other hand, white-collar workers have more control over what they do and thus have less stressful jobs.

Balfour (2002) reports on a 30-year study on civil servants, called the Whitehall Study, carried out by London University. The study found that low control, low involvement in decision-making, high job demands, low social support at work, and high effort combined to low rewards, leads to stress in the workplace. The lowest incidence of heart disease was found among the highest-level employees. This was contrary to expectations, as it was thought these individuals would suffer from executive stress. It seems that senior people have more control and thus are not as prone to heart disease, which got worse in the lower grades. It was discovered that death rates were three times higher in the junior grades than among the senior civil servants but only 40% of the difference could be explained by lifestyle choices, such as diet and exercise. This means that 60% was due to high control and status in the organisation.

Equity theory

People expect rewards to be in proportion to the effort expended. They expect to be paid fairly in relation to other employees and similar grades outside the company. If not, feelings of relative deprivation are experienced.

When dealing with others, they also expect to be treated fairly. When they perceive that they have been treated unfairly, they feel distressed and are motivated to restore equity. This is the prime moving force behind many industrial relations disputes concerning wages and working conditions.

People who perceive they are being treated fairly at work are less likely to experience emotional distress.

Effort / Reward imbalance theory

Effort is the mental or physical energy expended to achieve work-related goals. Reward is the compensation or acknowledgement in the form of pay, improved working conditions, status or career advancement.

The combination of high work demands, low job security, few career opportunities and poor reward systems is a major source of stress. The sense of injustice felt by the perception of poor pay and conditions in relation to the effort put in by workers is often reflected in industrial relations disputes. On the other hand, high effort and high reward conditions result in a happy and contented workforce.

Psychological contract

The psychological contract is an unwritten understanding that employers and employees have about their expectations from each other. The explicit contract is that the employee exchanges time, experience, expertise and knowledge for a reward package. The implied contract includes elements like loyalty, commitment, trust, equity, and security.

Under the old psychological contract, people entering employment expected good wages or salaries, training and development, career opportunities and security of employment. In return, they gave their time, education, expertise, experience, loyalty and commitment to the employer.

Under the new psychological contract, employees are no longer guaranteed jobs for life and are responsible for their own career development. Nonetheless, they are expected to be flexible, accountable, hardworking and committed.

Employees must now provide for themselves the security previously provided by employers. This means the employee will try to become as marketable as possible by building a portfolio of skills, through appropriate experience and continuous learning and development. Thus, employees are more likely to be loyal to their own personal development and future careers and less likely to be totally loyal, committed and willing to make sacrifices for the good of the company.

Many employees have seen their own parents being made redundant after years of loyal service and commitment. This implied breach of trust has given many new employees a negative perspective of employers' loyalty to employees. Thus the modern generation are less likely to be loyal to their employers. Thus, if the opportunity arises, they will have no hesitation in moving to a better job.

STRATEGY, STRUCTURE & STYLE

Strategy

In a competitive world, companies are forever trying to discover more cost-effective ways of transacting their business. The reduction of payroll costs is often a prime target.

Depending on market conditions, different strategies are appropriate from time to time. Strategies of expansion or divestment can be equally stressful for both managers and employees caught up in them. Mergers, acquisitions and divestments can be especially stressful. Culture clashes between merged companies and cost cutting bring their own stresses.

Redundancies are the most stressful situations for most employees, especially the older ones who will find it difficult to get new employment. For those who remain, reorganisations, transfers, relocations, increased workloads, and retraining are some of the problems faced.

Structure

The stressors caused by structure include:

- **Bureaucracy:** Bureaucratic structures are inherently stressful for those who have to work in them. Bureaucratic organisations, by their rule-bound nature and autocratic management styles, stifle initiative and creativity. They attribute blame and punishment rather than encouraging creativity and innovation and celebrating success and learning from mistakes. Close control of activities, strict discipline, frequent monitoring of results, rigid hierarchical structures, and lack of participation, all contribute to high levels of stress.

- **Functions:** Some functions, such as finance and marketing, have an interface with many other functions and the outside environment. By definition, these jobs have high role conflict and are potentially very stressful. Frequent interactions with people outside one's function may create stress. People in other functions often do not understand jobs outside their own areas and, as a result, make unreasonable demands and impose deadlines that are difficult to meet. Because of conflicting objectives, personality clashes and territorial infighting, interdepartmental conflict and power struggles are normal aspects of most organisations and ongoing sources of stress.

- **Politics:** To achieve anything worthwhile in organisations, one must get the support and co-operation of other people. People achieve objectives by forming coalitions with others. Failure to do this successfully can cause frustration, resentment and ultimately stress. People skills become more important as one climbs the managerial ladder. Promotion anxiety is a major stressor for many young executives eager to progress.

- **No training and development:** Often those selected for management positions are specialists or technicians with no prior experience, or knowledge, of management. Key skills for managers include financial management, influencing, conflict resolution, negotiating and chairing.

- **Non-participation:** People are usually motivated, if they are consulted about work-related issues and involved in the decision-making process. Employees have a fundamental need for a reasonable amount of control over their work and like management to acknowledge and appreciate their efforts at work. Participation is discussed in greater detail in **Chapter 9**.

Style

Management style itself can be a stressor:

- **Managerial styles:** Managerial styles can be autocratic, democratic or participative. In practice, the autocratic style is prevalent, even though lip-service is widely paid to the participative style of management. The modern workplace is a major source of stress because of its long hours culture, heavy workloads and (sometimes) atmosphere of bullying and harassment. In addition, work is often not appreciated, employees feel undervalued and have little sense of importance. In practice, managers rarely thank or praise their staff. A demanding job may not be stressful if the employee is valued, appreciated and supported by management. *Increased social support in terms of leadership, trust, respect, open communication and participation go a long way to reducing organisational stress.*

- **Monitoring stress levels in the workplace:** Managers and supervisors should take responsibility for monitoring stress in the workplace. Managers who adopt an active and visible managerial style of managing by wandering about will quickly spot problems such as work over-load, dangerous practices, bullying, victimisation, harassment and discrimination. These problems can be quickly nipped in the bud rather than being allowed to fester and eventually to explode into major industrial relations disputes. *In this regard, prevention is better than cure.*

- **Authority *versus* responsibility:** Authority must be commensurate with responsibility. A frequent source of managerial tension, anxiety and stress is the mismatch between formal and actual powers. Managers are put in the position where they are held responsible for something without having the formal power to achieve it. The manager may also have to make decisions quickly without recourse to sufficient information. Because they are responsible for the outcome of such decisions, they find the process stressful.

- **Self-management:** In stressful conditions, managers with the relevant skills, abilities and experience perform better than those without them. *Self-management skills, including time management, problem-solving, delegation, communication, and conflict resolution, enable a manager to manage more effectively.*

- **Lack of clear goals:** Goals provide a sense of purpose and direction. Being committed to goals acts as a motivator and an antidote to stress. However, unless goals are supported by an action plan, they remain merely aspirations. Note that unrealistic expectations are a major source of stress.

- **Bad boss syndrome:** Type A managers (see **Chapter 5**) are often very demanding and lacking in interpersonal skills. They work long hours and often their staff feel they have to do likewise, in order to show their commitment and loyalty to the company. Bad bosses often react to situations rather than plan. This crisis management style creates stress for their staff. *A variety of policies and programmes are available to reduce potential stressors in the workplace, including health promotion programmes, employee assistance programmes, free health insurance, and health and safety programmes.*

INTERPERSONAL RELATIONSHIPS

Work relationships are probably one of the greatest sources of organisational stressors. A large proportion of stress at work comes from poor interpersonal relationships, personality clashes, backbiting, misunderstandings, and breakdowns in communications. Managers who lack sensitivity are a major concern. For example, many criticise staff in front of colleagues or customers, which can be extremely stressful for the person involved. Learning how to relate to, and interact sensitively with, others is a key managerial skill. A manager needs to be able to relate well with their own managers, their staff, colleagues and customers.

Relationships of staff with managers

If the manager is seen as considerate and supportive, then the staff will give their friendship, trust, respect and loyalty to the manager. Managers who are low on consideration and high on task lack people management skills and are insensitive to the emotional needs of their staff. Staff of such managers experience more job pressure. Such managers do not give criticism in a helpful way, but instead play favourites with staff, pull rank, belittle staff in front of others, and take advantage of their staff whenever they get the chance. Staff want managers who can inspire them with a vision that they can buy into.

Relationships of managers with staff

People are more stressful to manage than things. Managers from technical backgrounds are often lacking in people management skills. They are used to things that do not talk back rather than people that do. Managing other people means you must communicate with them, motivate them, reward and reprimand them as appropriate. Building rapport with people and gaining their respect can be a very time-consuming process, requiring great patience from the manager.

There is a maxim in management that you can delegate authority but you cannot delegate responsibility. Thus, the manager is ultimately responsible and will be held accountable for the decisions of their staff. One should ensure that the people delegated to are willing and able to perform satisfactorily the work delegated. However, employees often complain that their managers are reluctant to delegate. Thus, the manager is overworked and the staff do not get the opportunity to grow and develop. Delegation is a visible way of demonstrating trust in your employees.

These days, managers are expected to adopt a participative approach to management. This puts further demands on the interpersonal relationship skills of managers. Some managers do not wish to be participative, as they see it as undermining their power base. They see their role as making decisions – sharing this role with staff is viewed as a dilution of power and a source of further stress for the manager.

Relationships with colleagues

These can be a source of great support or a source of great stress. Social support at work is essential to one's health and wellbeing. One spends a lot of time at work, so it's important to surround oneself with people that one respects, trusts and gets along with. Competition for promotion, office politics, backbiting, misunderstandings, poor communication, and personality clashes are just some of the things that can cause stress in the workplace.

Relationships with customers

Customers now expect the highest standards and demand to be treated in a courteous and professional manner. People who work in departments that interface with customers have a difficult job to do which require interpersonal relationships skills of the highest order including listening, empathy, patience and diplomacy. However, sometimes, customer expectations are not met and the reaction may be disappointment, annoyance, anger and, on rare occasions, violence.

When Relationships Go Wrong

Just as there are dysfunctional relationships within families, there are also dysfunctional relationships within the workplace, caused by violence, stereotyping, conflict, status, and diversity issues.

Violence by work colleagues

Authoritarian management styles, excessive discipline, tight controls, and strict job performance standards, giving employees little control over their jobs, are thought to be some of the factors that trigger off workplace violence. Communication problems between management and workers are often the root cause of violence in the workplace. Employees may feel they are being treated unjustly, talked down to by management, and generally resent the lack of respect they experience in the workplace.

Violence is not confined to bodily harm but also includes verbal intimidation, psychological abuse, stalking, bullying, threats and sexual harassment. Bullying and sexual harassment are explored in **Chapter 9**. The legal implications are dealt with in **Chapter 6**.

Work colleagues, customers or members of the public may perpetrate violence. On average, 20 workers are murdered each week in the USA, making murder the second highest cause of workplace deaths and the leading one for women. There is a rising incidence of violence in US colleges. Disgruntled students, armed with guns have murdered fellow students and teachers. Postal workers in the USA have experienced so many fatalities due to violence brought on by job stress that the term 'going postal' has crept into our language.

Violence by customers / members of the public

In the retail business, employees are often the subjects of violence due to armed robberies. Incidents include syringe attacks, kidnap, pistol whipping, and the use of knives, iron bars and sledgehammers. Some employees have been killed in such attacks. *Workstress.net* (January 2003) reports that nearly half of shop workers have taken time off because of violence. USDAW, the shopworkers' union, claim that thousands of its members live in daily fear of physical attack and verbal abuse by customers.

Verbal and physical abuse is a daily event in more than a third of stores, most commonly when young people are refused alcohol. On average, at least one shop worker is attacked every hour of the working day. The union maintains that managers should play a crucial role in dealing with the problem, and should be trained to reduce risks at work, deal with dangerous situations and support staff after an attack. USDAW is campaigning for adequate staffing levels, extra security at opening and closing times, closed circuit television and well-lit car parks.

Aircraft cabin crew are sometimes exposed to stress brought on by disagreeable, abusive and violent passengers acting out air rage. Scientists maintain that air rage is due to cabin pressure, oxygen levels, and the stress of being in a confined space. However, workers on the front line maintain alcohol is the most common cause; another cause is the fear of flying.

Stereotyping

Blondes are dumb. Americans are loud. Scots people are mean. Germans are hardworking. Irish people are fond of drink. Women are warm, kind, emotional, gentle, understanding, able to empathise and be helpful to others. On the other hand, men are aggressive, forceful, strong, rational, self confident, competitive and independent. Old people are set in their ways and incapable of learning new things. These are just some of the stereotypes that one frequently comes across. They are based on misinformed opinion rather than fact. For example, men and women, apart from the obvious physical differences, are remarkably similar.

To stereotype people is to categorise them according to a preconceived idea about the group that they belong to. Stereotypes are often applied to members of a particular religion, race, class, group, occupation or gender. Stereotyping influences the way we perceive and behave towards other people. Because of stereotyping men and women are channelled into particular roles. Stereotyping may result in prejudice. Being on the receiving end of prejudice is not pleasant and may be quite stressful for the victim.

Conflict

Conflict is the antagonism or active warfare that exists between individuals, groups or departments within a company. Personality clashes between managers and employees are a major source of stress in organisations. Office politics and competition between departmental managers may be intense. Different professions and trades frequently vie with each other for status and power; demarcation disputes over who should do what are a frequent source of industrial relations disputes. Competition for promotion and scarce budgetary resources may be a source of conflict.

The adversarial tradition between unions and management is a constant source of tension, friction and stress in organisations. Role relationships, such as those between boss and subordinate, are a primary source of conflict. Grievances, disciplinary matters, and performance appraisal are major sources of conflict between management and staff.

Conflict resolution is dealt with in **Chapter 11**.

Status

Another source of conflict is status differences between departments. Depending on economic circumstances and the culture of the organisation, some departments have greater status and power than others. For example, in some organisations, marketing may have the greatest influence and power whereas, in others, it may be finance. The perception by other functions that finance, through its budgetary and auditing responsibilities, has a policing role causes resentment and stress in many organisations. Production people often resent the fact that marketing people have a greater profile within the company and spend their time wining and dining clients. Sometimes, power differences are based more on perception rather than reality.

Diversity

Managing a diverse workforce requires many different skills such as sensitivity to other peoples' culture, traditions, beliefs and values. For example, a manager may have to make special arrangements to cater for the religious and dietary needs of staff who are members of the Muslim community. Similarly, a tolerance and acceptance for the way people from other cultures dress may need to be encouraged and supported in the workplace. *It is important that managers in charge of a diverse workforce are appropriately trained.*

TASKS

Lack of job satisfaction, poor job design, shift work, mobility and job performance are the key issues relating to tasks that cause stress in the workplace:

- **Job satisfaction:** Lack of job satisfaction due to repetitive routine work, as machines and robots have replaced many jobs previously conducted by humans. In many manufacturing jobs, employees have become equipment monitors, following procedures without much discretion, rather than technical experts.

- **Poor job design:** Little control over work, no consultation and insufficient reward for the efforts expended are three major sources of work stress. *The principles of method study, job enrichment and ergonomics can be used to improve the design of work.*
- **Shift work:** Many employees today work on a shift basis, often over 24 hours. It is now recognised that shift work is an occupational stressor. Frequently-changing shifts are stressful biologically, socially and emotionally. Shift work affects blood temperature, metabolic rate, mental efficiency and sleep patterns. People have a limited attention span and need plenty of rest and sleep. Family life is disrupted and because, of the unsocial hours, social life is severely hampered. It is ethically irresponsible to have those engaged in dangerous activities or in charge of other peoples' lives, work unduly long and unbroken shifts.
  The most efficient system of shifts has "day people" who work always during the day, and "night people" who always work during the night. The night people get used to working at night and sleeping during the day; it takes several weeks for a person's circadian rhythm to adapt.
- **Mobility:** Some companies expect their executives to be mobile and to move around the country or even around the world at their behest. Many managers comply because they fear that they might lose their jobs or that their careers might suffer, as mobility is seen as an inherent part of career development. In practice, the manager's family life is often disrupted and put at risk. Moving house several times in one's career can also be very distressing and unsettling for a family. Managers are not encouraged to get involved in the local community, because of lack of time and the knowledge that they will be moving on in a few years' time. Social relationships are sacrificed in exchange for careers. In dual career families, this type of lifestyle is rarely sustainable.
- **Job performance:** Performance appraisal can be stressful for the manager and the employee being appraised. It is considered the most unpopular of all management practices. Appraisal in relation to performance-related pay is particularly stressful. The manager has the onerous responsibility of making a judgement regarding the employee's job performance, which has long-term implications for the employee's standard of living and future in the company. From the employee's point of view, a once-a-year performance appraisal will be more stressful for the employee than continuous assessment. *Managers should be trained in how to*

run effective performance appraisals and in particular, how to give clear constructive feedback to the employee, enabling them to do their jobs more effectively. Listening, empathy, and rapport building skills are particularly useful. Managers need to be particularly sensitive, tactful and honest in giving bad news. Trained proficiency in this area will reduce the manager's exposure to potential stressors.

THE COST OF STRESS

It is now accepted that stress-related illnesses cost organisations a great deal of money each year. *Workstress.net* (Winter 2002) reports that a survey by the Trade Union Congress (TUC) in the UK found that work-related stress reported to unions has increased 12-fold in a year. Nearly 6,500 people made claims for stress in 2000 compared with 5,000 in 1999. Compensation awards in 2001 were £321 million, slightly more than the previous year. Public sector staff are most likely to claim work-related stress, but there are also claims from middle managers in manufacturing. The TUC called on employers to prevent work-related stress by assessing risks and adapting jobs to workers, rather than workers to jobs.

A 1996 report from the UK's Institute of Management maintains that an estimated 270,000 people take time off work each day due to work-related stress. This represents a cost of £7 billion annually.

A cost/benefit analysis should be undertaken by the company to identify the costs involved in a stress management programme compared with the benefits and savings involved. This analysis will show that stress management programmes make economic sense and make a significant contribution to bottom line results.

Costs

The following are some of the costs associated with stress in the workplace:
- Legal and compensation claims.
- Medical expenses.
- Health and safety issues, such as a poor accident and safety record.
- Misuse of drugs and alcohol.
- Absenteeism through lost working days.
- High labour turnover.
- Low productivity.

- Poor timekeeping and missed deadlines.
- Poor employee and customer relations.
- Suicide – in Japan, *karoshi* or death from overwork, is recognised as a fatal combination of stroke, high blood pressure, and stress.
- Divorce and marriage separations.
- Poor company image due to bad publicity in the media such as litigation concerning stress-related illnesses.
- Staff replacements and training.
- Stress related diseases.
- Long-term disability.
- Premature death.
- Stress management programmes.

Benefits

There is nothing philanthropic about an organisation taking measures to counteract stress in the workplace. It just makes good commercial sense to do so. Effective stress management will reduce the number of grievance and disciplinary disputes. As a result:

- The organisation will have lower costs for support services, like counselling and industrial relations.
- Staff will spend more time at work being productive rather than being absent due to stress-related illnesses.
- Sick pay and administrative support costs will also be saved.
- The costs of litigation against the company will be reduced (the legal aspects of stress are dealt with in **Chapter 6**). Substantial damages have been awarded against companies for cases of work over-load that lead to nervous breakdown, bullying, sexual harassment or discrimination.
- The reputation of the company will be enhanced making it easier to recruit able and suitable people for its work requirements.

Many of these savings can be quantified and compared with the costs of running stress management and employee assistance programmes.

CAREER MANAGEMENT

Managers are considered to have a career, as opposed to a mere job. This presupposes a high degree of commitment to the company and to one's own personal development.

Managers develop their careers by moving horizontally between departments and vertically up the hierarchy.

High commitment and loyalty is part of the developmental process and is considered essential if one wants to get promotion up the management structure. This means that a management career is going to absorb most of a person's time, with little time and energy left to devote to personal, social and family life. A manager's sense of identity often becomes totally absorbed in their job. This is the hidden psychological contract and the price the manager must pay if he or she has ambitions to get to the top.

Four stages of career management

The psychologist Super (1957) identified four career stages:

1. **Exploration stage:** This occurs between the ages of 15 to 24. During this time, individuals explore career opportunities and make choices regarding the type of organisations they wish to work in. This is often a time of great excitement, enthusiasm, innovation, and creativity in one's life.

2. **Establishment stage:** This occurs between the ages of 20 to the early 40s. During this period, individuals are concerned with establishing themselves in the organisation, and in society in general, and with progressing up the management hierarchy. They also have the onus of providing for the financial and emotional needs of their family. Managers sometimes take up part-time studies at this time, such as MBAs and other professional qualifications, in order to help them in their careers. Together with holding down the responsibilities of a full-time job, this puts many an executive under severe pressure.

3. **Maintenance stage:** This is the age from mid-40s to retirement. For most, this is a period of consolidation rather than trying to progress further. There is more competition and career opportunities are fewer. Most managers reach a plateau in their careers at this stage.

4. **Decline stage:** This is the stage where people start thinking about retirement and a life beyond work. This period is characterised by

a decreasing involvement and participation in work and is usually reached between 60 and 65.

All of these stages bring their own problems and challenges. Awareness of the stages should help a manager anticipate and plan for the stressors likely to be encountered.

Promotion, demotion and frustrated ambitions

These are all potential stressors:

- **Promotion:** Learning a new job, getting used to the unfamiliar, and taking on more responsibilities is a great challenge for most people but can be stressful for some. Over-promotion is where a person is given responsibility beyond their capabilities. The Peter Principle states that people are ultimately promoted beyond their level of competence, to the point where the requirements of the job exceed their capabilities. This, of course, can be a source of stress. Under-promotion is where the job under-utilises the person's ability and thus they have no opportunity to use their talents, education, expertise and experience. Like over-promotion, this may also be a source of stress.
- **Demotion:** Most people identify strongly with their jobs. Thus demotion and the loss of identity, pride and status involved in relation to peers can prove to be very stressful for some people. Demotion can also have difficult financial consequences for the person concerned. As people get older, demotion or lateral transfer may be the only option apart from redundancy.
- **Frustrated ambitions:** Many people in organisations have not attained the position that they desire or aspire to. Perhaps they are in the wrong jobs or working for the wrong organisation or lack the political skills necessary for advancement. When people's job or career aspirations are not met, bottled-up feelings of frustration cause tension and, ultimately, stress.

Dual careers

How to balance the demands of dual careers with raising a family is one of the key issues of modern living. The changing role of women in society means that they are now holding down jobs as responsible as, or even more responsible than, those of men. There is now less time to take care of family responsibilities because of work. In addition, in the past, wives often provided an emotional supportive role for their husbands. This antidote to stress cannot now be provided if they are committed to their own careers and work long hours.

Male attitudes have not kept pace with the changing role of women, so that working wives often carry the major burden of household duties resulting in a great deal of stress for them. This is taking its toll in the health of career women, who are now as prone as men to getting cancer and heart disease.

Promotion involving relocation may be a source of friction and tension between those with dual careers, causing further stress. Women are no longer willing to meekly follow their husbands' careers, as they have their own career paths to pursue. Disagreement and friction between the dual career partners is the ultimate result, since the male ego still believes that a man's career should take preference over that of a woman's.

Because of the aging population profile, and the demise of the extended family and the support of neighbours, there are an increasing number of employees who also carry the burden of looking after elderly relatives in addition to dual career responsibilities and their own family.

Many psychologists and sociologists believe that dual careers are one of the main reasons for the high rate of divorce in the Western world. Few organisations offer the type of flexible working arrangements and family friendly policies that dual career families need to support their lifestyles.

SUMMARY

The mnemonic RESIT will help you remember the major organisational stressors. RESIT stands for:

- Role
- Environment
- Strategy, structure and styles
- Interpersonal relations
- Tasks

Role includes ambiguity, conflict, over-load and under-load. Role ambiguity refers to a lack of clarity on how to perform one's job. Role conflict occurs when an employee experiences conflicting demands from different sources. Role over-load means that you have too much work to do. Role under-load means you have too little work to do.

The environment can be a major source of stress in the workplace, and includes noise and dangerous working conditions.

Dysfunctional interpersonal relations include violence, stereotyping, conflict, status and diversity. Poor work relationships are probably one of the greatest source of organisational stress.

The psychological contract is an unwritten understanding that employers and employees have about their expectations of each other. Jobs for life are a thing of the past. Job insecurity brings its own concerns and pressures.

Strategy, structure and style are just some of the organisational stressors causing problems for managers and employees.

Inappropriately-designed tasks create poor job satisfaction and performance appraisal is a potential source of stress for many employees.

Organisations should do a cost/benefit analysis on stress. The cost of stress includes litigation, health and safety and stress management programmes.

There are four career stages: exploration, establishment, maintenance and decline. Each stage has its own unique sources of stress.

Mismatch, overpromotion and frustrated ambitions are just some of the career issues that cause stress. How to balance the demands of dual careers and raising a family is one of the key issues of modern living.

5: STRESS IN INDIVIDUALS

- What is a Type A and Type B personality?
- How does attitude affect stress?
- What is transactional analysis?
- How does ability affect stress?
- What is the locus of control?

◆

We have to change our patterns of reacting to experience. For our problems do not lie in what we experience, but in the attitude we have towards it.
Akong Rimpoche

Mind Map of Chapter 5

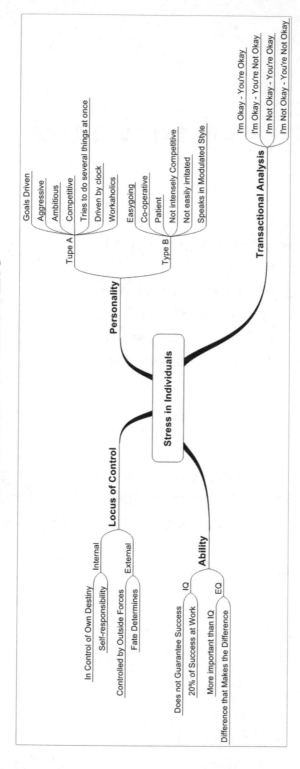

Personality

Tupe A
- Goals Driven
- Aggressive
- Ambitious
- Competitive
- Tries to do several things at once
- Driven by clock
- Workaholics

Type B
- Easygoing
- Co-operative
- Patient
- Not intensely Competitive
- Not easily irritated
- Speaks in Modulated Style

Transactional Analysis
- I'm Okay - You're Okay
- I'm Okay - You're Not Okay
- I'm Not Okay - You're Okay
- I'm Not Okay - You're Not Okay

Stress in Individuals

Locus of Control

Internal
- In Control of Own Destiny
- Self-responsibility

External
- Controlled by Outside Forces
- Fate Determines

Ability

IQ
- Does not Guarantee Success
- 20% of Success at Work

EQ
- More important than IQ
- Difference that Makes the Difference

A Type A personality is driven and subject to more stress than a Type B personality, which is laid-back. Optimists cope better with stressful situations than pessimists. In transactional analysis, those who adopt the 'I'm okay – You're okay' life position suffer least stress. Emotional IQ is considered more important than IQ to success in life. People with an internal locus of control experience less stress than those with an external locus of control.

TYPES OF PERSONALITIES

Type A and Type B personalities are based on research by Friedman and Rosenman (1974).

Type A characteristics

These include:

- Driven by goals.
- Aggressive: They don't tolerate fools gladly.
- Ambitious.
- Competitive.
- Tries to do several things at a time.
- Driven by the clock: they have an obsession with achieving more and more in less and less time.
- Workaholics, unable to wind down and enjoy leisure time.

The Type A personality is frequently found in managers on the way up. It is a most useful personality for one who is ambitious and hopes to move up the management hierarchy. Because of their ambition and aggression, type A personalities are not renowned for their good interpersonal relationship skills.

It is not Type A characteristics of themselves that are injurious to one's health, rather it is the cynicism, hostility, aggressiveness, anger and time urgency frequently inherent in this type of personality which does the damage.

Type A's self-esteem and sense of identity depends on their achievements. If they fail to achieve something, they become frustrated and angry. Being aware of Type A characteristics will help you identify them in yourself so that you can take steps to reduce them. This is possible because Type A characteristics are mostly learned and thus, with some effort, can be unlearned.

While Type A characteristics may get you to the top, it is the Type B characteristics that will keep you there. The most successful senior executives tend to be Type B.

Type B characteristics

These include:

- Easygoing: able to set time aside for fun and relaxation without a feeling of guilt.
- Cooperates with others: believes the best in people rather than the worst.
- Patient.
- Is not intensely competitive.
- Not easily irritated.
- Speaks in modulated style.
- Has a more balanced, relaxed approach to life: work is only one of many interests.
- Concentrates on one thing at a time.

Type Bs are less likely to suffer from stress-related illnesses. They tend to be calm and content, laid-back, take things in their stride, are good at delegating, trust and co-operate with others and like themselves.

Health-wise, it would pay every one of us to acquire Type B characteristics, as Type B people are less prone to heart disease and other stress-related illnesses. With the proper mental discipline, Type B characteristics can be learned.

OUTLOOKS ON LIFE

Optimism

Optimists see the glass as half-full. They see things in a positive light and expect to experience favourable outcomes and results. High self-esteem and self-efficacy means that optimists exploit opportunities and seek out challenges.

People with high self-esteem feel good about themselves. Such people are less likely to interpret an event as stressful. In addition, they cope better when stress does occur. This creates a positive reinforcement cycle that further enhances their self-esteem and ability to cope with stress.

Self-efficacy means that a person believes that they have the necessary ability and skills to successfully carry out a particular course of action. Such people use problem-solving strategies and seek out social support. People who feel competent to act correctly and successfully in specific situations are less likely to experience stress. Those with low self-efficacy, believing their abilities and skills are poor, find such situations stressful.

Optimists are more stress-resistant than pessimists. For example, if a person with an optimistic outlook is asked to do a difficult project at work, they are likely to think, 'It will be a lot of extra work, but I know that I will succeed. Moreover, it will give me an opportunity to learn new things and develop my skills further. It may also further my chances of promotion in the future'. This individual may experience some stress but, unlike the pessimist, it is unlikely to lead to distress, and will only serve as a positive motivator to do a good job.

Studies show that optimists work harder, go further in their careers, make more friends, make more money and are more likely to be creative than pessimists are. It seems that optimists are particularly equipped to handle the everyday trials and tribulations of life. It's a question of when the going gets tough, the tough get going, and the 'tough' are more likely to be optimists.

Pessimism

Pessimists see the glass as half-empty. They view situations negatively and expect to experience unfavourable outcomes and results. They moan and groan and dole out nothing but doom and gloom. They usually have self-limiting beliefs that prevent them from undertaking new challenges. They avoid goals that they feel will cause stress to achieve.

A person with a pessimistic outlook, if asked to take on a difficult project, is likely to view the increased responsibilities negatively, thinking, 'I'll never be able to do this project and the boss will realise how incapable I am and fire me'. Anxiety and distress may follow, leading to feelings of hopelessness and depression. In the future, this individual is likely to procrastinate when faced with difficult tasks.

The average person is reputed to have about 50,000 thoughts a day. Negative thoughts make up about 60%. Reduce them by substituting positive thoughts for negative thoughts. For example, the minute you start feeling stressed by entertaining a negative thought, stop and say to yourself: 'I will remain serene and calm in this challenging situation'. This thought-stopping and substitution strategy is effective for coping with stress.

TRANSACTIONAL ANALYSIS

Harris (1969) describes four fundamental life positions:

1. **I'm okay – You're okay:** People who hold this position see themselves as interdependent with others and their environment. They are self-confident and are comfortable with themselves. They view others as likewise. They are more likely to seek social support and network with others. They have no difficulty asserting themselves, being open and discussing their problems with others. Because they see others as okay, other people will reciprocate in a similar fashion.

2. **I'm okay – You're not okay:** People who adopt this position consider that they can only rely on themselves. They consider other people as worthless and potential enemies. They are suspicious of others and blame everybody else for their problems. They consider it pointless to speak out, as nobody will do anything about it anyway.

3. **I'm not okay – You're okay:** People who adapt this life position have an inferiority complex. They lack self-confidence and have low self-esteem. If they have problems, they are to blame because they are incompetent or lack sufficient influence to change events.

4. **I'm not okay – You're not okay:** People with this life position consider themselves and others equally worthless. They are consumed with negative feelings. They feel disconnected from others and from their environment. They tend to become loners obsessed with their own problems and concerns.

From a work point of view, adopting the "I'm okay – you're okay" life position means that you are positive about yourself, assertive and capable of delegating. These three skills are particularly appropriate if you want to avoid work over-load by saying 'No' and delegating effectively. A willing workhorse will eventually collapse under the load.

The last two life positions are the most stressful because you take a negative view of your own capabilities. If you don't feel good about yourself, you are unlikely to win the respect of others and accept praise, even if it is genuinely earned.

ABILITY

IQ does not guarantee success in life. There are many people with high IQs who are sociopaths and failures in life. Emotional intelligence (EQ) is now considered to be just as important or even more important than IQ.

Consider the problems caused by emotionally-immature people in the work situation, ranging from tantrums to actual incidents of verbal abuse and physical violence. EQ is now thought to be the difference that makes the difference between those people who get ahead in the workplace and those who are left behind. EQ is the ability to recognise and manage one's own feelings and being sensitive to the feelings of others.

IQ only contributes about 20% to our success in work. The rest comes from how to deal with our emotions and the emotions of others. People who get to the top are likely to have the ability to get on with others. Social skills such as facilitating, cooperating, coordinating, coaching and influencing are very important for managers. Good managers are able to read others accurately, make good first impressions, and built rapport quickly. They are sensitive to the needs and concerns of others.

LOCUS OF CONTROL

Locus of control is the expectancy that personal actions will be effective in controlling the environment. It is the perceived source of control over one's own behaviour. If you think you have control over your own destiny, then you probably have. If you think you haven't control over your own destiny, then you probably haven't. People vary on a continuum ranging from internal to external locus of control.

Internal locus of control

People with an internal locus of control believe that they are in control of their own destiny. They take responsibility for their own actions, do not over-react to people or situations and refuse to see themselves as victims. In education, they are more motivated to achieve academic excellence.

When 'internals' confront a stressful situation, they believe that they can have an influence on the results. Therefore, they take control of the situation. They believe that hard work and application of skill is what makes things happen rather than luck or fate.

Internals tend to be assertive, get on with life, and do not see themselves as victims. They are less anxious and better able to deal with frustration. They take setbacks in their stride, rather than seeing things as a major catastrophe or blaming fate. Thus they perceive many situations as less stressful than people with an external locus of control.

External locus of control

People with an external locus of control believe that their lives are controlled by outside forces. They believe that what happens to them is due to fate, luck or the actions of others.

When "externals" confront a stressful situation, they believe that they have little effect on the results. Because of this attitude, they often lack initiative and take a passive approach to life and its problems. Rather than taking action to reduce the stress, they are likely to be defensive and do nothing. Because they feel helpless, powerless and anxious, they perceive situations as more stressful than people with an internal locus of control. They are more anxious and less able to deal effectively with frustration.

SUMMARY

Research has established that Type A personalities are more prone to various types of stress-related illnesses than Type B personalities. Type A personalities are driven, while Type B are more laid-back.

Generally, optimistic people experience less stress than pessimistic people do. Optimists see the glass as half-full while pessimists see it as half-empty.

An understanding of transactional analysis helps us to cope more effectively with stress. The 'I'm okay – you're okay' life position means that you are positive, assertive and capable of delegating and less prone to stress.

Generally, people with higher IQs experience less stress than those with lower IQs. A high IQ is not necessarily a guarantee of success in life.

Emotional intelligence plays a greater part in success than IQ. Emotionally intelligent people handle stress better than others do and generally lead more successful lives.

People with an internal locus of control experience less stress than those with an external locus of control.

6: LEGAL ASPECTS OF STRESS

- How does employer liability for stress arise?
- What can employers do to avoid litigation?
- What major lawsuits have been taken concerning stress?
- What is vicarious liability?
- What is the relevant health and safety legislation on stress?

◆

Morality cannot be legislated, but behaviour can be regulated. Judicial decrees may not change the heart, but they can restrain the heartless.
Martin Luther King, Jr.

MIND MAP OF CHAPTER 6

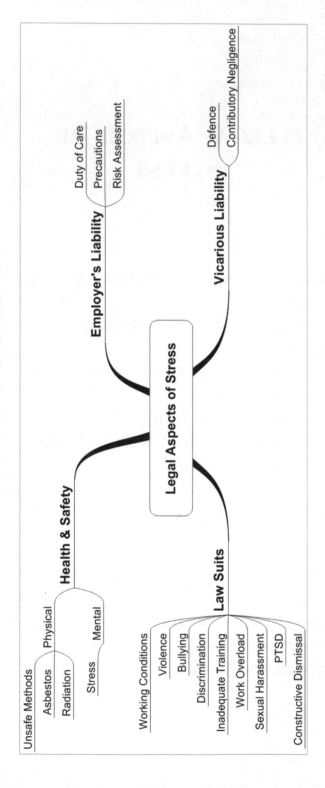

Legal Aspects of Stress

Employer's Liability
- Duty of Care
- Precautions
- Risk Assessment

Vicarious Liability
- Defence
- Contributory Negligence

Health & Safety
- Unsafe Methods
  - Physical
    - Asbestos
    - Radiation
  - Mental
    - Stress

Law Suits
- Working Conditions
- Violence
- Bullying
- Discrimination
- Inadequate Training
- Work Overload
- Sexual Harassment
- PTSD
- Constructive Dismissal

The prospect of litigation for stress-related illness due to working conditions is a major concern for most organisations. Organisations may find themselves liable under common law, criminal law and health and safety legislation. Successful law suits have been brought against organisations for stress-related illnesses caused by violence, bullying, personality clashes, post-traumatic stress disorder, work over-load, sexual harassment, discrimination, inadequate training and constructive dismissal.

Litigation stress is the anger, frustration, irritability and anxiety felt by those who are the object of malpractice suits. Some of these lawsuits drag on for years, adding to the stress experienced. Awards have been made against employers such as the army and police for post-traumatic stress disorder. Employers who fail to address bullying, discrimination and sexual harassment in the workplace are leaving themselves open to future litigation. *Many cases would not arise if employees were treated with respect and dignity.*

EMPLOYER LIABILITY

Duty of care

Under common law, employers have a duty of care to their employees to keep them safe from harm. Similarly, the employer has an implied duty under the contract of employment. In addition, employers have a statutory duty under health and safety legislation to safeguard the physical and psychological health of their employees. Employers who put excessive pressure on employees for results may be in breach of this duty of care, although employers may assume that employees are able to withstand the normal pressures of work.

The employer is not liable for stress caused outside the workplace due to personal or family issues.

Precautions employers can take

To meet their obligations, employers should take reasonable precautions such as:

- Taking particular precautions with susceptible employees by providing stress counselling. An employer who offers a confidential advice service, including counselling or treatment facilities, is unlikely to be found in breach of duty.

- Conducting regular performance appraisal reviews to give employees an opportunity to raise concerns before they become major issues.
- Implementing a grievance procedure, so that complaints can be brought to the attention of the employer.
- Designing jobs to avoid stress as much as possible, since employers may be liable for injury that is reasonably foreseeable.
- Keeping up-to-date with health and safety requirements and legislation.
- Having a safety statement, in accordance with health and safety legislation. The employer has an obligation to continually revise this statement in line with changing circumstances.
- Making sure that employees wear appropriate protective clothing and pointing out to them the dangers of not doing so.

Risk assessment

Employers should carry out a risk assessment so that preventative and protective measures against stress can be taken. Reliable questionnaires, in conjunction with other methods such as consulting staff, should be used.

Workstress.net (Summer 2003) reported that the Health and Safety Executive (HSE) in the UK carried out interviews in early August at a Dorset National Health Service hospital, which had failed to address issues of increased work-related stress among its 1,000-plus staff. The HSE's investigations followed staff complaints of bullying and excessive hours. It was revealed that management had no procedures to assess the risks of stress and thus fulfil the duty of care to employees. West Dorset General Hospital NHS Trust was required to carry out a full risk assessment of the burdens being placed on employees at Dorchester County Hospital. This was the first enforcement notice to be served on a British employer to control workplace stress, which costs Britain about £3.7 billion a year. The Trust could face substantial fines, or prison terms for its senior executives.

Since stress is a hazard that should be included in the risk assessment, employers should consider whether any employees are being placed under excessive pressure, as it is accepted that occupational stress is more likely to occur in such an environment. The vulnerability of those with excessive workloads should be considered and appropriate action taken as necessary. *Good employers will have a stress policy in place.*

Vicarious liability

An organisation may be responsible for the acts of its employees, expressly or implicitly authorised by the employer. This means that, if one employee suffers injury because of the negligence of another employee, the employer will be held liable.

The injured employee could sue the individual responsible for the injury, but in practice they will sue the employer, since the employer is insured against personal injury claims.

An unauthorised act, or one outside the scope of the employee's job, is not deemed to be done in the course of employment. In addition, evidence of precautionary steps taken by the employer may be used in defence against claims.

Contributory negligence is where the employee is partly to blame for the injury. The compensation paid by the employer to the employee may be reduced by an appropriate amount to reflect *pro rata* the extent of negligence on the employee's part.

LAW SUITS

There are now frequent press reports of employees being awarded substantial sums in successful litigation against employers held liable for stress-related illnesses. *Managers should be trained in stress management and in particular to identify early stress symptoms in employees.*

Employers may be liable to pay damages for distress, grief and inconvenience, lost earnings, future loss of earning until retirement, refund of medical expenses and provision for future medical expenses, and costs of litigation. It may cost less to prevent stress than to cure it, making stress management a good investment.

Dangerous working conditions

Employers may be liable for claims arising out of occupational stress caused by dangerous physical and psychological conditions at work. In one case that came before the Irish Courts, a worker was awarded IR£35,900 for being exposed to asbestos and the potential risk of contracting cancer (*Sunday Business Post*, 2 February 1997).

The employee, O'Byrne, was found to have developed a form of anxiety state that arose from the fact that his employers, the B&I Line, negligently exposed him to a life-threatening risk. Whether or not O'Byrne ever contracted a disease was considered irrelevant by the court, which held that the B&I Line was obliged to compensate him for the mental anguish he suffered. Of the total award, IR£10,000 was allocated for future medical costs and expenses.

The Irish Health and Safety Authority has recently classified environmental tobacco smoke (ETS) as a class A carcinogen and as dangerous to workers as exposure to asbestos dust. This increases the hospitality sector's exposure to potential legal claims for ETS in the future. Smoking in the workplace is now illegal in Ireland.

Violence in the workplace

In Ireland, a Revenue official who was assaulted in the course of his work was awarded IR£15,000 against his employer, because of the trauma he endured (*Sunday Business Post*, 2 February 1997).

Stress News (11 January 2000) reports that a Council worker, Mr. Randy Ingram, was awarded £203,000 out-of-court for stress involving depression against Hereford and Worcester County Council. Mr. Ingram managed sites for the Council, housing disruptive gypsy families who physically and verbally abused him. During his work, Mr. Ingram had been shot at and attacked by a dog. Council officials undermined his position and failed to support him by siding with the gypsy families.

The main problem was the Council did not apply a consistent policy when dealing with the tenants on the sites so the managers overturned the warden's decisions. It was alleged that seven out of the 10 wardens employed by the Council had taken time off work due to stress. One warden had left on grounds of ill health and received £14,500 compensation.

Legal costs

The following are some examples of the legal cost of stress in the workplace:

BULLYING

- In July 1998, Anthony Ratcliffe, a deputy headteacher, was awarded £101,028 compensation in an out-of-court settlement against Dyfed County Council for being bullied and humiliated by his headteacher (Smith, 1998).
- In an Australian judgement in December 1996, a District Court Chief Judge awarded more than $170,000 (about €90,000) damages for failure on the defendant's part to exercise due care in managing the working environment (Carter *v* Pinewave). The judge held that the plaintiff suffered acute psychological torment from his employers. Thrust into a management position despite

lack of managerial experience, and faced with massive company expansion and appalling working conditions, the plaintiff collapsed. He was diagnosed with a depressive disorder that left him incapable of making the most basic decisions and contemplating suicide (Sheehan, 1999).

DISCRIMINATION

- A dyslexic factory worker at CL Plastics, Birkenshaw, was bullied by his colleagues for 18 months until he left. In one incident, they shrink-wrapped him, almost causing suffocation. When he complained, management failed to take action. The Leeds tribunal, which awarded him £28,000, found that he had suffered discrimination because of his disability and had been constructively dismissed (*Stress News*, 28 February 2000).

INADEQUATE TRAINING

- In Lancaster *v* Birmingham City Council, a settlement of £67,000 was made to Mrs Lancaster. She had been re-deployed into a job for which she was completely untrained and the employer ignored her report that she was out of her depth. Liability for a stress-related illness was admitted at the door of the Court in July 1998 (Smith, 2000).

- In 1999, Mrs Beverley, a former housing officer, was awarded £67,000 compensation against Birmingham City Council for occupational stress. This made legal history, as it was not an out-of-court settlement. The council admitted that it was legally liable for her illness. As her job became more demanding, the council failed to provide the necessary management support and training and, as a consequence, she suffered from depression, anxiety, and panic attacks.

WORK OVERLOAD

- Walker *v* Northumberland County Council showed that stress-related personal injury claims could be brought against employers. John Walker, a social worker, successfully sued his employer after his second nervous breakdown. His workload had significantly increased and extra resources had been promised but not provided. His out-of-court settlement, in 1996, was for £175,000. This case paved the way for similar stress-related legal actions (Earnshaw & Morrison, 2001).

- A delivery firm was fined £2,500 after a 19-year-old driver, who worked up to 16 hours a day, was killed in a car crash. It is believed the driver, Gary Couser, fell asleep at the wheel and died when his car hit a pile of stones in West Lothian. The employers pleaded guilty to a charge of allowing Couser, to drive excessive hours without appropriate rest periods. Couser was the only one of the firm's 12 drivers whose vehicles were not fitted with a tachograph to record driving hours (*Workstress.net,* January 2003).

SEXUAL HARASSMENT

- Strathclyde Regional Council *v* Porceilli involved sexual harassment by Mrs Porceilli's male colleagues, including suggestive remarks and brushing up against her. Her claim that such behaviour constituted unlawful discrimination, on the grounds that because of her gender she had been treated unfavourably, was upheld and an award of £3,000 was made against her employer (Cartwright and Cooper, 1997).

- In a case involving alleged sexual harassment by pupils in a County Wicklow School, two female teachers were awarded damages. The legal action claiming discrimination and victimisation was taken by the Association of Secondary Teachers in Ireland (ASTI) on behalf of the teachers. An equality officer awarded IR£12,000 to one teacher and IR£7,000 to another, recognising that schools were liable for the action of pupils (*The Irish Times,* 26 January 2001)

POST-TRAUMATIC STRESS DISORDER

- A retired policeman, Eamon Melvin, of Gort, Co. Galway who suffered serious post-traumatic stress disorder (PTSD) as a result of a work incident, was awarded IR£305,298 compensation by the High Court. He brought his claim under the Police Compensation Acts. It arose out of the murder of Ms Philomena Gillane, whose husband got an eight-year jail sentence for soliciting two men to murder her. In the course of the investigation, Mr Gillane threatened to kill Mr Melvin. Consequently, Mr Melvin became anxious, frightened, paranoid and seriously worried about his personal safety and his heart condition worsened. The award included IR£150,000 compensation for distress suffered (*The Irish Times,* 4 July 2000).

- Lloyds TSB made an out-of-court settlement of £100,000 to a 27-year-old employee who suffered stress at work. Leslie North, who ran the Southam branch, was diagnosed as suffering from post-traumatic stress disorder. He said that the problem began when he had to meet increasing sales targets without support. He was put under intolerable pressure, working until 2 am to keep up with his work. The award was the first of its kind in the financial services sector. Lloyd TSB did not admit liability. Further cases of

PTSD are likely to follow in the future, due to bank rationalisation programmes in which closures of bank branches and reductions in staff levels place more work and responsibility on remaining staff (*Stress News*, 14 August 2000).

CONSTRUCTIVE DISMISSAL

- A former investment director with ICC Venture Capital (now owned by Bank of Scotland), Ms Prisca Grady, settled her constructive dismissal case for an undisclosed amount. Ms Grady claimed that she was forced to resign after bullying and sexual harassment traumatised her. She claimed that, after her resignation from her job in mid-2000 she became depressed and suicidal and for some months spent most of her time in bed (*The Irish Times*, 23 October 2002).

- In Caroline Aspell *v* Sherlockstown Enterprises Ltd, the claimant, who was manager, was certified as suffering from acute stress because of her situation at work. This followed a number of incidents between herself and the company director about her days of work, job performance, and staff discount scheme. While the claimant was on sick leave, she received further letters from the company director. These stated that she would be demoted on her return to work from sick leave. The claimant subsequently claimed constructive dismissal and the tribunal awarded her IR£11,000 in compensation (*Sunday Business Post*, 3 December 2000).

HEALTH & SAFETY LEGISLATION

This differs from country to country but usually covers such areas as:
- Unsafe methods.
- Machinery.
- Protective clothing.
- Building sites.
- Asbestos dust, which produces fibrosis of the lungs and can cause cancer.
- Coal dust.
- Radiation.
- Benzine.
- Dangerous chemicals.

The EU Framework Directive on Health and Safety recognises that employers should deal effectively with stress in the workplace.

Organisations have a legal responsibility under Health and Safety legislation to take reasonable care to ensure that employee health is not placed at risk through excessive and sustained levels of stress. *It pays employers to take workplace stress seriously as it may cost them dearly in litigation, out-of-court settlements, sick pay and in having a de-motivated and under-productive workforce.*

SUMMARY

Employers have common law, contract of employment and statutory obligations for the health and safety of their employees, including their psychological and physical welfare.

The employer has a duty of care not to create employment conditions that would harm the health of employees. The employee, on the other hand, has a duty to take reasonable care.

Vicarious liability means that the employer may be liable for the acts of an employee. Evidence of precautionary steps taken by an employer may be used in defence against claims. Where the employer is partly to blame for the injury, contributory negligence may be taken into account when settling the claim.

Employees may take a case against their employers for alleged constructive dismissal as a result of unreasonable treatment at work.

There have been some major legal cases taken against employers concerning stress. Cases of sexual harassment, discrimination, constructive dismissal, work over-load, post-traumatic stress disorder, violence and bullying have been successfully prosecuted before tribunals and the courts. Inadequate training has been an issue in some cases.

Health and safety legislation now recognises that stress can be a source of illness in the workplace and that employers can be prosecuted for placing employees in a stressful working environment.

7: CHANGE

- What are the types of change?
- What is the change model?
- What are resistors, hesitators and early adopters?
- How does organisational change occur?
- What is technostress?
- What is information overload?

◆

We trained hard – but it seemed that every time we were beginning to form into teams, we would be reorganised. I was to learn later in life that we tend to meet any new situation by reorganising; and what a wonderful method it can be for creating the illusion of progress while producing confusion, inefficiency and demoralisation.
Petronius

Mind Map of Chapter 7

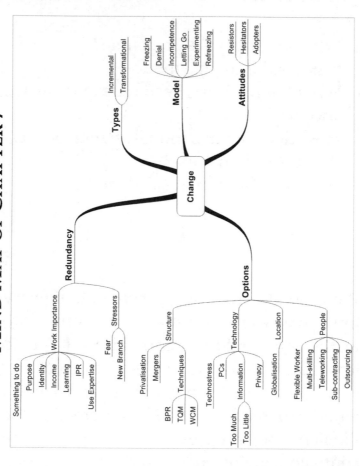

Types
- Incremental
- Transformational

Model
- Freezing
  - Denial
  - Incompetence
- Letting Go
- Experimenting
- Refreezing

Attitudes
- Resistors
- Hesitators
- Adopters

Change

Redundancy
- Work Importance
  - Something to do
  - Purpose
  - Identity
  - Income
  - Learning
  - IPR
  - Use Expertise
- Fear
- Stressors
  - New Branch

Options
- Structure
  - Privatisation
  - Mergers
  - Techniques
    - BPR
    - TQM
    - WCM
- Technology
  - Technostress
  - PCs
  - Information
    - Too Much
    - Too Little
  - Privacy
- Location
  - Globalisation
  - People
    - Flexible Worker
    - Multi-skilling
    - Teleworking
    - Sub-contracting
    - Outsourcing

All change is accompanied by stress. The change model goes through six stages: freezing, denial, incompetence, letting go, experimenting and freezing. The attitudes people adopt to change have been categorised as resistors, hesitators and eager adopters. Eager adopters suffer the least amount of stress.

Change usually applies to structure, technology, physical location and people. Redundancy is one of the most stressful life events that an individual can experience. Technostress is the term used when people are unable to cope with new technology. Information overload is where people are unable to cope with all the information that is currently available. Globalisation means that multinational companies are willing to relocate to lower cost economies, despite the distress and financial hardship this causes employees.

CHANGE

Stress is synonymous with change. Anything that causes change is likely to cause stress. It doesn't matter whether the change is beneficial, it still will cause a certain amount of stress. For example, marriage is a positive change but, because of the degree of uncertainty and adjustment involved, it will inevitably bring a certain degree of stress.

One expects negative changes such as redundancy, illness, or moving house to be stressful events. Even worrying about imagined situations may cause stress. Employees who actively embrace change and who can cope with ambiguity are more likely to survive in today's highly turbulent company environments.

To master stress, we must change. We may need to change some or all of:
- Our behaviour.
- Our beliefs, attitudes and values.
- The way we think.
- Our lifestyle.
- The situation we find ourselves in.

However, there are also lots of things beyond our control that we cannot change – for example, environmental changes such as economic recessions and market downturns. Also, we cannot change other people. Only they can change themselves.

Accepting what we can change and what we cannot change will save us a lot of distress. Remember the old saying, 'we should have the courage to change the things we can, the serenity to accept the things we can't, and the wisdom to know the difference'.

Types of change
Transformational or discontinuous change is the type of change involved in the break up of the USSR and the fall of the Berlin wall. The abrupt change from a planned economy with universal healthcare and food for all to a private economy where many cannot afford healthcare and nutritious food has created massive change and transformational stress. Similar change is often experienced when a nationalised industry becomes privatised.

Deregulation has brought much change in its wake. At an organisational level, business process reengineering can cause massive organisational change and transformational stress.

Incremental change is usually more acceptable and less stressful for employees. This has a stress inoculation effect as employees get gradually acclimatised to the change.

The change model
You are more likely to manage change successfully and experience less stress if you understand and anticipate the typical stages people go through in the change process.

The stages of the change model are:

- **Freezing:** You experience shock at this stage, particularly if you perceive the change is for the worst. For example, the fear of losing your job may immobilise you. You may feel trapped because the solution to the problem is outside your control. This feeling of helplessness and powerlessness can be very stressful. As we are creatures of habit, most people's first reaction is to resist change. Morale, productivity and overall work performance is low at this stage.
- **Denial:** This is a coping mechanism. People deny that the change is taking place. This helps them cope with the situation and the fear of the unknown. This avoidance technique helps you to process the unwelcome information subconsciously, get on with your job, and come to terms with the change over time. In the short-term, work performance may improve as people concentrate on their work and forget about their problems.
- **Incompetence:** You under-perform because you are now reluctant to adapt to the change. Anger and resentment, usually directed at management who are blamed for the situation, replaces your

sense of shock and disbelief. You may feel that your past loyalty and commitment to the company has been betrayed.

- **Letting go:** You start to come to terms with the change. This stage is sometimes called unfreezing. You let go of the past and embrace reality. You become more positive about the change.
- **Experimenting:** You take on the new way of doing things and abandon old methods. As a result, performance starts to improve.
- **Refreezing:** This is the consolidation stage, where you accept that the past is dead and buried and adopt the new ways of thinking and behaving. Feelings of depression are replaced by optimism, you forget about the past, and you get on with your new life.

Attitudes and change

Employees caught up in change caused by new technology often experience an emotional roller-coaster. Those who accept the change and try to influence what is going on are likely to suffer less stress. Those who resist technical change can become very emotional and even experience a certain degree of distress. Some writers have called this state 'technoanxiety', which is the same as technostress.

Attitudes towards technological change have been categorised as:

- **Resistors:** These are people who do not enjoy technology, do not like new technology and do not want technological change. Some of these people are even technophobic or very fearful of new technology. Resistors have a negative attitude towards technology and will be reluctant to use it, unless forced to do so. Their productivity is lower as a result.
- **Hesitators:** These people have a 'wait and see' attitude. They are not technophobic, but want to monitor the technology. They know that new technology often has problems in the initial stages, so they will wait until the problems have been sorted out before they adopt it.
- **Eager adopters:** These are people called 'technophiles', and are naturally enthusiastic about any new technology and will take it up as soon as it is released. They expect problems with new technology but find the process of solving the problems enjoyable and stimulating.

Resistors and hesitators are more likely to find the everyday hassles such as slow computer speeds, illegal input messages, computer crashes, and e-mail viruses more stressful than the eager adopters who are fascinated by all facets of technology.

Change options

Change usually applies to structure, technology, physical location or people. Many organisations are currently going through a process of rationalisation or restructuring. This usually means redesigning the organisation to reduce costs or to suit current circumstances, resulting in great technological change and disruption for managers and employees alike.

STRUCTURE

Structure as a change option can involve downsizing, privatisation, mergers, acquisitions and divestments, or new techniques and philosophies.

Downsizing

Downsizing is a process undertaken by management to improve the efficiency, productivity and profitability of an organisation. It is achieved by improving work processes, reducing the workforce and cutting costs.

Delayering is the vertical reduction of the number of managerial levels in the organisational structure. It results in fewer levels in the hierarchy with more work, responsibility, and decision making being thrust upon the remaining levels.

Downsizing (or 'rightsizing') and delayering are often euphemisms for redundancy and usually mean a much greater workload for the surviving employees, who also start to worry about their own job security.

These cost-cutting measures have become an acceptable way of increasing company profitability. In the process, employees experience greater job insecurity, lower morale and become less loyal to the company. In addition, they often become risk-averse and indecisive.

The psychological contract between the employee and employer is eroded or broken and trust is compromised. It is very hard to be committed and loyal to an organisation that shows little commitment and loyalty to you. People who are made redundant lose their self-esteem and self-confidence, rapidly developing feelings of worthlessness, hopelessness and inferiority.

Privatisation

Privatisation (or denationalisation) is the transfer of ownership of an industry or firm from the State to private industry. In the past few years, airlines, airport authorities, water authorities, rail and bus transport, radio and TV stations, telecommunications, and electricity are just some of the organisations that have been privatised. In local government, services such as bin collection have also been privatised. Major restructuring and changes in policies, procedures and working practices have affected the lives of thousands of employees.

Some of these organisations have brought in early retirement packages. Managers who previously had aspirations to go further have been offered early retirement instead. For some, this is a very traumatic and stressful time. Downsizing means that there are fewer promotional outlets available. Cuts in government spending mean that managers have to operate within very tight budgets. Job vacancies are not filled immediately, resulting in staff taking on more responsibility in the interim with little or no monetary reward. All of these changes have exposed employees to greater stress.

Mergers, acquisitions and divestments

A merger is where two or more firms combine on a mutually agreed basis authorised by the firms' management and shareholders. Unlike a merger, in an acquisition, the management of the target firm often opposes the acquisition. Although a 51% stake is sufficient, most companies prefer to have complete control in order to avoid interference from minority interests.

When one company takes over another, there is often a clash of cultures causing conflict. Merging the minds and hearts of the employees is much more difficult than merging the structures of companies. Many people will suffer a crisis of loyalty and identity.

Divestment is where a company closes down or sells one or more of its operating units or a whole business division. The objective is rationalisation and cost reduction. Inevitably, mergers, acquisitions and divestments means redundancies, job changes and work overload for those who remain. Divestment because of the inevitable redundancies is more stressful for employees.

Managers made redundant often experience feelings of betrayal, loss, anger and fear about their future. Some experience intense shock and grief comparable to the death of a close relative. In some cases, employees who remain may be required to reapply for their own jobs and must go through the stress and humiliation of being interviewed for a job they previously held. The loss of face, uncertainty and insecurity involved is a great source of stress to many. Because of the time-consuming negotiations involved in mergers and acquisitions, human issues are often forgotten about and so the needs and concerns of employees during such a traumatic time are often overlooked.

New techniques and philosophies

Many employees consider new techniques and philosophies, such as Business Process Re-engineering, Total Quality Management and World Class Business, as just new ways of extracting more work from fewer employees. Some refer to them as 'management by stress'. Others consider that they are scientific management principles dressed up in new clothes. Managers make the case that they provide opportunities for greater job satisfaction. However, the real agenda is usually cost reduction.

TECHNOLOGY

Automation is the use of mechanical or electrical machines, such as robots, for frequently-repeated production processes to make them self-regulating, thus avoiding human intervention. Automation involves high capital costs but low labour costs. It is usually applied to mass production, assembly-line-type operations.

The outcome of automation is fewer people employed and the majority of those that remain in employment have less satisfying jobs viewing monitors, minding machines and following standardised procedures. A minority – highly-skilled technicians – have more satisfying jobs.

Technostress

Technostress, or technical stress, is a modern disease caused by people's inability to cope with new technology, particularly automation, computers and telecommunications. The information and communications technology (ICT) industry is generally regarded as being a stressful one in which to work, due to the rapid rate of change.

Rapid job obsolescence is now a feature of modern technological society. It is estimated that the average skill turnover is now about 10 years. Consider the rapid changes that have take place in recent years. Some workers view the need to acquire new skills as a threat to their existing skill self-esteem rather than an opportunity to grow and develop. Those who view technology as a threat rather than a challenge are more likely to suffer stress. *Adequate planning and training will reduce the anxiety of employees about technology. Studies show those who receive training have positive reactions to technology.*

PCs and stress

Personal computers and laptops are now an integral part of company life. Many people spend long hours in front of a computer screen. Studies have shown that prolonged work at visual display units (VDUs) causes health problems such as repetitive strain injury, headaches, eye problems, fatigue and psychological stress. The radiation given off by VDUs has been linked to miscarriages and serious medical conditions such as cancer.

Repetitive strain injury is also known as carpal tunnel syndrome. The symptoms of this include pain, tingling and numbness in the hand, wrist and arm. It is caused by continuous rapid use of fingers, and is common among those who frequently use keyboards. Ergonomically-designed chairs, computer desks and keyboards, and taking appropriate breaks are among the solutions to the problem.

Trying to keep up with new and changing software creates tension, particularly for older managers who may be set in their ways. Technology-related rage (TRR) is a term that has crept into the English language to describe the stress people feel when their computers response time is slow or they crash or don't perform to expectations. In addition, the threat of e-mail virus contamination is a growing problem causing annoyance, frustration and inconvenience.

Too much information

Complete encyclopaedias, textbooks and professional publications are available on CD-ROMs and DVDs. The Internet allows access to entire libraries of information. Rather than making us more effective, the sheer volume of information that we are daily exposed to may actually add to our indecisiveness, impair our performance and increase our stress.

Information over-load is also called Information Fatigue Syndrome. This is where managers are given more information than they can reasonably assimilate.

Reuters Business Information (1996) reports that information over-load makes many managers mentally and physically sick.

Emails in particular waste a lot of management time, because they have to be read before deciding that they are irrelevant. Instead of reducing workload, these have created information over-load. *Stress News* (25 February 2000) reports research published by the Institute of Management, which found that e-mail is now 10th in the league of stressors at work.

Too little information

Information under-load happens where managers are not given sufficient information of the right quality or detail to carry out their jobs effectively.

Some people are provided with information on a "need to know" approach based on the status and seniority of the individual rather than operational needs. Access to some corporate databases may be blocked for particular grades of staff. Because information is usually channelled through the management hierarchy on a seniority basis, it means that managers may take it on themselves either not to pass on the information or edit it. Consequently, operational staff are often the last to hear about strategic and policy changes.

Invasion of privacy

Closed circuit television (CCTV) is increasingly used to watch employees as they go about their work and to watch citizens going about their everyday business.

Many organisations are concerned about the high rate of fraud amongst their staff and use hidden CCTV as a means to detect fraud. Knowing that your every movement is being watched can be very intimidating and may add to the pressures of work.

Surveillance cameras on main streets, in public buildings, and in private companies to monitor the movements of people and to prevent crime are a feature of modern life. We are nearer to a police state than we realise.

Mobile phones, mobile email, pagers and fax machines now enable others to contact us at all times. Many employers see nothing wrong with contacting employees whenever they need them. With some people, this reinforces their ego needs, making them feel important and indispensable. Others find this practice an invasion of privacy and an additional unwanted stressor of modern living

PHYSICAL LOCATION

Globalisation is the expansion of a company into foreign markets by exporting and also by overseas investment in component factories, manufacturing plans, sales and marketing facilities and in research and development. Such companies do not rely on a single market but have an international presence. Multinational companies and globalisation are synonymous. Multinational companies have little loyalty to a particular country and have no hesitation in moving to other countries if cost considerations dictate. Many have relocated to India, Eastern European, or Far Eastern, low cost economies. Some multinationals are simply coordinators: production and other labour intensive operations are outsourced and subcontracted.

The result is closures and large-scale redundancies in Western economies. Employees' lives are put in turmoil, with mortgages to pay and families to support without a weekly wage to support them. Local shops and services also experience a slowdown in their business.

PEOPLE

Flexible working, multi-skilling, de-skilling, teleworking, sub-contracting, outsourcing and redundancy are some of the issues confronting people in the modern workplace.

The flexible worker

Globalisation has given rise to the concept of the flexible worker, who does not have a job for life but must move and retrain in line with the changing demands of the labour market.

Flexible jobs are often poorly-paid, casual or part-time with few benefits other than the wages drawn. Many flexible jobholders do not enjoy the benefits of union protection or collective bargaining. Without the security of a steady job or a pension scheme, the flexible worker can lead a precarious and stressful existence.

Multi-skilling and de-skilling

Multi-skilling and de-skilling are just two of the changes that people have had to cope with in the modern workplace.

Multiskilling is a system of working where employees are trained to work in various types of jobs, and none are kept on the same type of work for very long. The purpose is to facilitate flexibility in the deployment of the workforce.

De-skilling is the process of reducing the number of skilled jobs and replacing them with unskilled jobs.

Employees are now encouraged to manage themselves because of the rapid rate of technological change taking place and because close supervision is unwieldy and no longer cost-effective. Under self-management, workers are encouraged to identify with the objectives, values and philosophies of the company. In addition, new techniques and philosophies such as empowerment, World Class Manufacturing, Total Quality Management and Business Process Re-engineering have reinforced the self-management philosophy and changed the way work is organised and done. Both approaches may be strongly opposed by unions.

Teleworking

Working from home may be an option offered to some knowledge workers. It particularly suits journalists and writers, and knowledge workers in the business and financial services sector.

However, teleworking can result in social isolation and stress for some workers. The way forward seems to be people working a few days a week at home rather than full-time.

Sub-contracting

Many organisations now sub-contract work previously done by full-time employees, who become self-employed. This reduces the employer's head count and avoids the fixed costs of employment such as welfare, health insurance, and pension costs. Instead, the subcontractors become responsible for their own income tax, welfare, health insurance and pension costs.

Outsourcing

As well as sub-contracting, organisations are outsourcing workers and relying on temporary or semi-permanent staff to provide services that were once done by full-time employees, in order to cut costs and concentrate on core activities. Printing, cleaning, and canteen services are just some of the activities that have been outsourced in many companies. Although outsourcing reduces headcount costs, it does create feelings of insecurity and thus lack of employee commitment to the organisation.

Redundancy

Redundancy is now perceived to be more stressful than other major life events, such as divorce or moving house and second only to illness or death of family or friends. This is not surprising in our Western Society with its work ethic and where a person's identity is often closely associated with their work or profession.

The most common stressors linked to a change in job role or redundancy are:

- Fear of losing your job or being demoted.
- Financial insecurity.
- Loss of structure and purpose in one's life.
- Fear of losing the friendship of your work colleagues.
- Fear that your skills will become obsolete and the new skills will prove difficult to acquire.
- Fear of transfer or relocation.
- Loss of power and status.
- Increased workload.
- Changes in work colleagues and managers.
- The sense of rejection.
- Fear of new advanced technology and the need to acquire new competencies to deal with it.
- Lack of communication about the implications of the proposed change.

Good communication kills rumours and reduces the stress and anxiety experienced by employees during a transition period. The more employees are kept informed about future plans, the less stress and disruption they will experience when the plan is implemented.

Survivors' syndrome is the guilt the remaining employees have about the present and their uncertainty about the future. They feel guilty about their colleagues losing their jobs while they retained theirs. Work pressure increases on remaining staff. There is now the same amount of work or more work being done by the remaining staff. Although productivity may increase, organisations often lose valuable skills and experience, which are often irreplaceable.

Some companies that downsize their workforce often hire additional younger employees at the same time. Surviving employees' question the justice of this practice and wonder why the departing employees couldn't have been retrained for these new positions instead of being laid-off.

If downsizing is handled insensitively, then the surviving employees feel particularly vulnerable and aggrieved as their trust in the organisation has disappeared with the departing employees. On the other hand, the trust and respect of the surviving employees will be retained if the company has progressive and equitable HRM policies in place.

WORK

Work plays a very central role in our lives. For example, Margaret Thatcher, the former Prime Minister of England, when she lost her job, is reported to have felt very lost without her usual tightly-packed schedule. One day the world is dancing to your attention and the next you are effectively ignored: for an ex-Prime Minister, this must be particularly difficult and stressful to live with.

Redundancy may be perceived as the ultimate failure, particularly if a person has invested considerable loyalty, time and energy in their work.

The following are some of the reasons why work plays such a central role in the lives of many:
- It provides something to do.
- It gives purpose, structure and a sense of direction to one's life.
- It gives one a sense of identity and status.
- It provides a source of income to provide us with the comforts that we need in life.
- It may provide lifelong learning and career opportunities.
- It provides you with an opportunity to meet other people and make friends.
- It provides you with an opportunity to use your education, knowledge, expertise, experience and skills and to acquire new ones.

Our work can be a source of great satisfaction and pride. Consequently, the loss involved when one is made redundant is far greater than just the monetary loss. Having a job may be stressful but having no work is even more stressful.

SUMMARY

The types of change are transformational or discontinuous, and incremental.

The change model has seven stages:
1. Freezing.
2. Denial.
3. Incompetence.
4. Letting go.
5. Experimenting.
6. Refreezing.

In relation to new technology, people can be resistors, hesitators, or eager adopters. The eager adopters suffer the least stress.

Change options include structure, technology, physical setting, and people. Pressures on employees for increased productivity may cause stress.

Organisational change may be due to restructuring, privatisation, automation, or mergers and divestments.

Technostress is the inability of some people to cope with new technology. Information over-load is where people are unable to cope with the many sources of information currently available. Automation, computers and telecommunications are the major technological changes.

New techniques and philosophies such as BPR, TQM and WCM may bring radical change and disruption to the lives of employees and managers alike and are often viewed with suspicion of an underlying cost-reduction agenda.

Redundancy is one of the major life events causing great stress for both employees and managers.

8: GENERAL STRESS INTERVENTIONS

- What is the difference between primary, secondary and tertiary interventions?
- What are the general coping strategies?
- What is the stress problem solving approach?
- What are the habitual thinking errors?
- What is the ABCDE method of dealing with emotional problems?

◆

I'm an old man and have known a great many troubles, but most of them never happened.
Mark Twain

MIND MAP OF CHAPTER 8

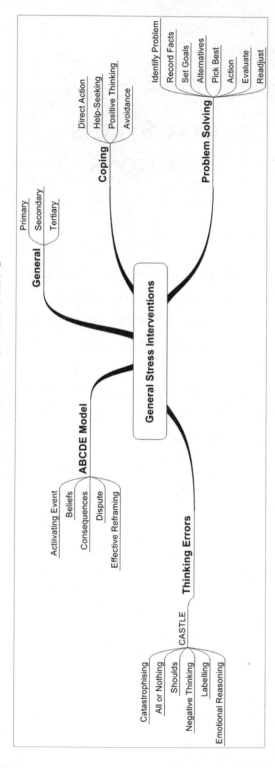

The basic interventions that a company can make to deal with stress occur at primary, secondary, and tertiary levels. Primary interventions tackle the root causes of stress. Secondary interventions help managers recognise and deal with stress-related problems as they occur. Tertiary interventions help employees recover from stress.

TYPES OF INTERVENTIONS

Primary

These interventions remove or reduce employees' exposure to sources of stress by adapting the culture, structure and functioning of the organisation, including issues of power and control. They deal with the *causes* rather than the *symptoms* of stress – thus they get to the root of the problem.

Primary interventions aim to promote a supportive and healthy work environment. A stress audit may be used to identify and deal with the causes of organisational stress.

Managers tend to view stress as an employee problem rather than one caused by the work environment or the company itself. Hence their preference for employee assistance programmes and stress management programmes to solve the employees' problems. In fact, working conditions, organisational structures, and leadership styles are often the chief source of job stress. Better shift arrangements, work-breaks, staffing levels, family-friendly policies, and participative management styles can all help to reduce stress at work.

Primary interventions can be at a personal or organisational level. At the personal level, personal development plans, social support systems and work-life balance will help to eliminate stress from the workplace.

At an organisational level, restructuring to create greater flexibility and increased knowledge-sharing throughout the organisation can be beneficial in counteracting stress. Organisational policies such as cutting down on long working hours, introducing flexible working hours, or anti-bullying policies are often more effective than stress management courses or employee assistance programmes.

Personal interventions include:

- Planning one's own career development, by creating a personal development plan.
- Getting involved in social events and networking. Organisations can facilitate this process through social clubs and the provision of leisure facilities.
- Eliminating the source of stress by creating an appropriate work/life balance. This can be helped by family-friendly policies within organisations.

Organisational interventions include:

- Fair reward systems.
- Flexible work patterns.
- Participation – lack of consultation and participation in decision-making is a major source of stress.
- Communication – organisational goals and expectations should be matched. Employees should be kept informed about the business and operations of the company.
- Teamwork – teamwork increases the sense of identity that employees have with their work group and organisation.
- Fair employment practices, such as anti-discrimination and anti-bullying policies.
- Re-design of structures, systems, procedures and jobs. Job conditions such as heavy workloads, infrequent rest breaks, long working hours, shift work, meaningless work, and lack of control are just some of the situations that cause job stress.

Secondary

These interventions, which operate mainly through stress management training, improve management's ability to recognise and deal with stress-related problems, such as anxiety and depression, as they occur. They aim to increase stress awareness, improve resistance to stress, and help employees to manage stress more effectively.

Stress management training may cover such topics as health, exercise, relaxation, meditation, biofeedback and reframing techniques. Skill training may include interpersonal relationships, time management, problem-solving, conflict resolution, leadership, delegation and communication. Such programmes are known to produce positive short-term benefits, but the long-term benefits are doubtful if the primary causes of stress are not tackled and eliminated.

Tertiary

These interventions help employees recover from stress caused by work-related problems.

Employee assistance programmes (EAPs), health programmes, health circles, and counselling may be cost-effective, attractive to employees and socially-responsible. However, while it is important to help, support and counsel employees on a one-to-one basis, EAPs still do not tackle the primary causes of stress.

In general, secondary and tertiary interventions are aimed at the individual employee. Primary interventions are mostly aimed at the organisational level. In practice, primary interventions are the most effective in tackling stress but are relatively rare. Secondary and tertiary inventions are tantamount to shutting the stable door after the horse has bolted. Most employers prefer to deal with the symptoms of stress rather than the causes, with few offering to reduce hours, redesign jobs, introduce flexible working or eliminate workplace bullying.

GENERAL COPING STRATEGIES

Coping strategies are practical and psychological actions a person can take to manage situations where the perceived demands are greater than their personal resources to deal with them. It is through effective coping strategies that we reduce or eliminate stress in our lives. The specific stressors experienced will determine the appropriate coping strategies, or combination of coping strategies to use.

The four main coping strategies are:

1. **Direct action:** This is where the individual adopts a systematic problem-solving approach to identify and solve the particular stressful situation. Problems may be prioritised and dealt with accordingly.
2. **Help-seeking:** This is where the individual seeks the social support of managers, supervisors, professionals, family and friends to help them get through a stressful situation. For example, supportive management and family-friendly policies can reduce the stress experienced by dual career families.

3. **Positive thinking:** This is a psychological approach where the individual decides to manage their thoughts in an optimistic way, such as affirmations, visualisation, and reframing. This does not change the stressor but may minimise the negative feelings associated with it. For example, humour or prayer has been found to be an effective stress reducer in situations where the life stressors cannot be removed or changed, such as in terminal illness.

4. **Avoidance/resignation:** This is where the individual attempts to avoid the stress, or hopes time will take care of the situation, or is resigned to the fact that there is nothing than can be done about it. In a work situation outside the control of the employee, this strategy might be useful. However, in a situation where the employee could exercise some influence on the situation, this strategy may exacerbate the feelings of having no control and prevent the employee from taking appropriate action.

THE STRESS PROBLEM-SOLVING SEQUENCE

People who adopt effective problem-solving strategies are less likely to suffer stress than those who do not. When things go wrong, they look for possible solutions.

The problem-solving sequence is as follows:

- **Identify the problem and its stressors:** Symptoms may help you identify stressors but should not be confused with them. Managers should be trained to identify the signs of stress in their staff. *Management by walking about is a good way of keeping in touch with what is going on in the workplace. A stress audit may be used to ascertain the causes of organisational stress.*

- **Record the facts:** Use a stress audit together with face-to-face interviews of key personnel to gather as much information about the problem as possible. Use concise, clear and concrete language when compiling your questionnaire or interviewing staff. Identify those factors that make the situation a problem. Separate facts from assumptions. List the main stressors identified and link them to categories of workers, locations and departments.

- **Set realistic goals:** To deal with stressors, it is best to set goals. Addressing the problem as a series of sub-goals can solve most serious problems, since the problem thus becomes more manageable.

- **Develop alternatives:** Most problems have many solutions. Use brainstorming principles to generate alternatives. This approach ensures that nothing is likely to be overlooked and the best and most effective solution will be ultimately discovered.
- **Pick the best alternative** or combination of alternatives. The potential of these in meeting the defined goal should be evaluated. Both the short-term and long-term effects of the proposed solution should be considered. *Remember that the best results are achieved by tackling the primary causes of stress.*
- **Take action:** Prepare and implement an action plan. Action may be taken at the primary, secondary, and tertiary levels. Choose to work at managing stress, and change the things that are causing stress, rather than drifting along waiting for others to take action.
- **Evaluate:** Monitor the consequences and success of the plan. Has the stress intervention worked; if not, why not? How does the actual outcome compare with the anticipated outcome?
- **Re-adjust** strategy, if necessary, to take the findings of the evaluation stage into account. Remember that fighting stress in the workplace is an ongoing process rather than a once-off effort.

HABITUAL THINKING ERRORS

Our beliefs, attitudes, emotions, and thoughts determine the way we interpret and feel about a particular situation. Change your thoughts and you can change your feelings. Sometimes, when we are stressed about a situation, it is due to a distortion in our thinking.

The most common thinking errors can be recalled by the mnemonic CASTLE:

- **Catastrophising:** This is where you magnify your problems, imperfections and shortcomings. For example, 'This is a disaster, I'll never be able to overcome this problem'. Learn to take setbacks in your stride. Conversely, you may minimise your strengths, resources and good points and thus fail to consider and exploit opportunities.
- **All-or-nothing thinking:** This is the way that a perfectionist thinks: everything is seen as black and white, right or wrong. There are no shades of gray in-between. Perfectionists set themselves impossibly high standards and anything less than excellent is seen as failure.

- **Should statements:** This is where you motivate yourself by shoulds, shouldn'ts, musts and oughts. Although you may prefer yourself, other people, things or circumstances to be different from how they actually are, you know there is no universal law that says they shouldn't or must be different. It is inevitable that many things will not be to your liking. Accept that uncertainty, frustration and disappointment are aspects of normal living.
- **Thinking negatively:** You make a negative interpretation of a situation, even though there are no facts to support your conclusion. You may assume what other people are thinking and negatively interpret reactions to you. For example, 'My manager dislikes me'. You may predict the worst outcomes – for example, 'I'm going to fail this exam'.
- **Labelling or mislabelling:** This is where you describe an event by using colourful and emotional language. If you make a mistake, you describe yourself as 'a total failure'. If somebody is rude to you, you describe them as 'ignorant and unmannerly'. The next time you label yourself or others in some way, stop for a moment and look at the evidence to support your conclusion. On a realistic and logical basis, you will find it difficult always to find supporting grounds for your negative evaluations.
- **Emotional reasoning:** This is where you let your heart rule your head when arriving at conclusions. You may interpret feelings as truth. For example, 'I feel guilty, therefore, I must have done something wrong'. You feel angry at the least provocation.

THE ABCDE PROBLEM-SOLVING MODEL

This is based on rational emotive behavioural therapy. This is an emotion-focused method rather than a problem-focused method. We are disturbed by our perception of events rather than the actual events themselves. ABCDE helps people deal with unhealthy negative beliefs and emotions blocking them from reaching their goals.

Common irrational beliefs include:

- Everybody should like us.
- Other people ought to facilitate and please us.
- Life must be always nice and pleasant.

For example, the ABCDE problem-solving approach may be used to help a person who is anxious about making a presentation before work colleagues, as follows:

- **Activating event:** This might be a potential workplace stressor like the prospect of making a presentation to colleagues at work. The stressor should be identified and written down in specific, clear, and concrete terms.

- **Beliefs:** A lot of stress comes from our beliefs. We have hundreds of premises and assumptions about all sorts of things that we hold to be true. In the case of presentation skills, our beliefs may include: that the presentation is going to be a disaster; that people will laugh at you; that you will dry up; and that the audience is going to be unsupportive and threatening. In addition, you may believe that, as a result of making a poor presentation, you will lose the respect of your work colleagues. Even worse, you may believe that it would be career suicide. Realistically, it is normal to experience some problems. However, logically anticipate likely problems and have contingency plans to deal with them when they arise. Preparation and practice is the key to success. You are unlikely to become an accomplished presenter without adequate planning, experience and practice.

- **Consequences:** This is the distress and anxiety felt as a result of entertaining irrational beliefs. The most important aspect of taking charge of a stressful situation is to develop emotional control. This is achieved by changing our attitudes, beliefs and thoughts towards the presentation.

- **Dispute the irrational belief.** That is, the belief that the presentation is going to be a disaster. That people are going to laugh at you. That you will be unable to handle questions if they arise. What are the facts to support these irrational beliefs? Beliefs become self-fulfilling prophecies, if you allow them to do and fail to question them. Beliefs should be theories or preferences rather than rigid rules. Change your ways of thinking in line with new information and evidence.

- **Effective:** Reframe with a new rational belief. You are now internalising a new outlook that will reduce the emotional stress of making a presentation. Your new thoughts might include that your presentation is going to be a success, and that people are going to respond in a friendly and supportive manner. Mentally rehearse by visualising the presentation in advance. See yourself giving a relaxed, interesting, dynamic and successful presentation. See a friendly, receptive and supportive audience and see yourself handling questions in a calm and competent manner. See the smiles and hear the applause when you complete your presentation. Experience the satisfaction and pride of a job well done. You are now using a performance-enhancing thought instead of a performance-interference thought. In addition, take practical steps to support your positive thinking, otherwise it remains mere wishful thinking. This means adequate preparation. Break down the necessary presentation skills into sub goals for research, handouts, content, voice, listening, handling questions, posture, eye contact, visuals, timekeeping and so on. Address each of these issues. Leave nothing to chance. Furthermore, prepare in advance for likely questions. If perchance a question arises that you do not know, throw it out to the audience for discussion. The probability is that someone in the audience will have the answer. If that doesn't work, admit that you do not know the answer but commit to research it further and come back to the member of the audience at a future time with the answer.

Remember the ABCDE method requires hard work and practice if you want to successfully overcome irrational beliefs. Practice makes perfect and practice makes permanent.

SUMMARY

Stress interventions can be classified as primary, secondary and tertiary. Primary interventions go directly to the root cause of stress. Secondary interventions aim to increase stress awareness, improve resistance to stress, and help employees handle stress. Tertiary interventions help employees recover from stress caused by work related problems.

The four coping strategies are: direct action, help-seeking, positive thinking, and avoidance/resignation. It is through effective coping strategies that we reduce or eliminate stress in our lives.

The stress problem-solving approach is useful when dealing with stress problems. The stages are: identify the problem, record the facts, set goals, develop alternatives, pick the best alternative, take action, evaluate and follow up.

The mnemonic CASTLE will help you recall the main habitual thinking errors: catastrophising; all-or-nothing thinking, should statements; thinking negatively; labelling and emotional reasoning.

The ABCDE approach is particularly suitable for dealing with emotional problems. ABCDE stands for: activating event, beliefs, consequences, dispute the irrational belief, and effective reframing.

9: ORGANISATIONAL STRESS INTERVENTIONS

- What training interventions can be used for stress?
- What job interventions can be used for stress?
- What is an employee assistance programme?
- What corporate programmes can be used for stress?
- What corporate policies can be used for stress?
- What culture change strategies can be used for stress?

◆

To preserve health is a moral and religious duty, for health is the basis of all social virtues. We can no longer be useful when not well.

Samuel Johnson

MIND MAP OF CHAPTER 9

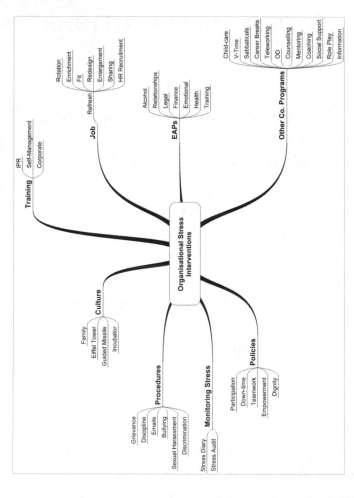

Training interventions for managing stress should cover a range of interpersonal and self-management skills. Job related strategies such as job enrichment, job enlargement and job rotation might be used to improve morale and job satisfaction. Employee assistance programmes (EAPs) may be used to help employees manage stress. Other corporate programmes might cover counselling, mentoring, coaching, and empowerment.

Procedures and policies should be put in place to handle grievance, discipline, bullying, discrimination and sexual harassment. Changing the culture of a company is a difficult and long-term process and different corporate cultures invoke different stress responses from employees.

TRAINING INTERVENTIONS

Types of training interventions useful in dealing with stress include: interpersonal relations, self-management and corporate programmes.

Interpersonal relations

Training in interpersonal relations includes:

- **Conflict resolution:** Managers tend to engage in conflict avoidance rather than conflict resolution. In conflict situations, managers tend to become more autocratic rather than participative. *Training in interpersonal skills would reduce the incidence of conflict avoidance and improve decision making.* Conflict resolution is dealt with in more detail in **Chapter 11**.

- **Assertiveness:** Learning to say 'No'. If you are unassertive, you may quickly take on too much work and become over-loaded and stressed. Assertiveness training, originally aimed at women, is just as useful to men. Assertiveness is discussed in more detail in **Chapter 11**.

- **Influencing and negotiation:** Interpersonal skills enable employees to deal more effectively with personal and inter-group conflict. *Empathy skills help managers deal sensitively with employees' fears and concerns.*

- **Confidence-building:** Self-esteem and positive thinking can be enhanced through transactional analysis. The use of affirmations and visualisation will also help you to become more confident.

- **Communication skills:** Managers should keep employees informed about what is going on in the company. If employees feel their concerns are being listened to, they are more likely to be co-operative and productive.

Self-management

Training in self-management can include:

- **Planning:** Failure to plan is planning to fail. Thinking ahead and creating contingency plans for likely scenarios will help your life run more smoothly. Actual results should be measured against sub-goals and corrective action taken to put the situation back on target again. In practice, many managers adopt a reactive approach rather than a proactive approach to management.
- **Problem-solving** and decision-making skills are the cornerstone of effective management. Procrastination and indecision are common problems in management.
- **Time management,** including delegation and avoiding interruptions and procrastination, will enable you to work more efficiently and effectively. Time management and delegation is discussed in more detail in **Chapter 11**.
- **Setting goals:** Without goals, you will achieve nothing worthwhile in life. Goals should be SMART (specific, measurable, achievable, relevant and timely). Goals give you direction and purpose and must be supported by action plans.

Corporate

Corporate training interventions to combat stress can include:

- **Stress management courses:** Many companies run stress management courses for their employees. In the right circumstances, such courses can be beneficial for employees, provided some action is taken at the primary level to tackle the root causes of stress. However, employees may be reluctant to go on stress management programmes because of the fear of admitting that they are under stress. Stress may carry with it the stigma of mental illness in a macho culture and, consequently, is perceived by some as a weakness.
- **Anger management:** Some Asian companies have acknowledged the need for employees to let off steam in a controlled way. They supply beanbags or cushions that employees can thump to get rid of their frustration and anger. Some Japanese companies allow employees to fire darts at images of managers to get rid of their frustrations.

- **Chairing meetings,** minute writing and presentation skills are essential to the effectiveness of any manager. Newly appointed managers should be trained in these skills.
- **Wellness or health promotion programmes:** These may focus on the employee's total physical and psychological health, including quitting smoking, controlling alcohol intake, exercise and healthy eating. Employees are encouraged to take responsibility for their own health. EAPs may be subsumed under wellness and health promotion programmes.
- **Retirement planning** courses can help employees make the transition successfully from work to retirement. These courses usually include health, financial and taxation issues and how to make use of your time in an enjoyable and productive way.
- **Stress policies:** A stress management policy should include basic information about the symptoms and potential sources of stress. *The statement should say that the organisation is committed, and accepts its responsibilities, to take appropriate action to prevent or minimise stress in the workplace.* It should indicate sources of information and help for those experiencing stress.
- **Anti-discrimination policies,** dealing with issues such as gender, age and race should be put in place, supplemented by equality awareness training for staff.

CORPORATE PROGRAMMES

Corporate programmes that work to reduce stress in the workplace take a variety of forms.

Job

The following are some of the interventions that a company can create to make work more enjoyable and stress-free.

The mnemonic REFRESH can be used for recall:

- **Rotation:** Job rotation is the systematic movement of employees between jobs, sections or departments within a company. The purpose may be to induct new employees, fill work gaps as needed, prevent job boredom or provide training and development for employees. Job rotation may also be used to give employees a rest from particularly stressful jobs.
- **Enrichment of job:** Job enrichment is also known as vertical job enlargement. It involves increasing a worker's responsibility and

control over their work. It usually involves giving the worker more demanding and developmental type work, requiring the acquisition and application of new competencies. Job enrichment is an effective motivational technique, where enriched jobs are significant, and provide a sense of identity, autonomy, and feedback. Bear in mind, that not all employees want an enriched job: some are happy to do routine work. Enriching the job of an employee with a low need for achievement or external locus of control may only increase anxiety. So it is important to match job enrichment with employees' individual needs and desires.

- **Fit:** Job fit matches the employee's skills, interests, qualifications and temperament to the job, avoiding square pegs in round holes. Use selection criteria and aptitude tests to eliminate those candidates who are unsuitable for particular jobs and who are susceptible to stress. Organisations should try to select those who are better able to cope with role ambiguity and conflict, responsibility for people, substantial workloads and the pressure of working to strict deadlines.

- **Re-design of job:** Poor job design may mean having too much work to do, working long hours, insufficient breaks, ill-defined tasks, inefficient methods, and inadequate resources. Some jobs are stressful because of the technology used or the nature of the tasks performed. *Ergonomics can be used to improve the interface between humans and machines. Method study can be used to improve job design by reducing the number of movements and processes.* Variety, feedback, autonomy, empowerment, and a sense of meaningfulness in the work will help to increase job satisfaction and motivation.

- **Enlargement:** This is also known as horizontal job enlargement. Job enlargement provides more variety of tasks, usually at the same level of responsibility. In the long term, providing a greater variety of tasks to do may not prove to be more motivational. However, both job enrichment and job enlargement will give the employee more skills and thus make them more valuable to the company, or more marketable outside.

- **Sharing:** Job sharing is where a full-time job is split between two employees, with the duties and responsibilities as well as the salary and benefits shared. Job sharing enables people to balance work, personal and home commitments. Job sharing must be co-ordinated by the employees concerned and by their managers to ensure that it works smoothly. *It is important that job sharers are* *given the same opportunities as full-time employees for promotion and personal development.*

- **HR Recruitment:** Recruiting the wrong person for a particular position may cause stress. It may be possible through psychometric testing to screen out at the selection stage people prone to stress. However, caution is necessary, as such selection methods – in some circumstances – may be considered potentially discriminatory.

Employee Assistance Programmes

EAPs offer a range of services including psychological advice, assistance or counselling. In addition to dealing with work-related issues that interfere with job performance, they also deal with personal problems such as relationships, money problems, alcohol and drug addiction.

The range of services offered by EAPs will differ from one organisation to another. Typically, they cover:

- Alcohol- and drug-related problems.
- Family, marital and relationship issues.
- Legal and financial difficulties.
- Work-related problems.
- Emotional problems.
- Health-related issues such as smoking, eating disorders, and diet.

The objective of EAPs is to help employees return to making a full contribution to the organisation. They may be run by the HR function or bought in as an outside service offered by consultants. The employee's supervisor may refer the employee, or the employees may initiate action themselves.

The heart of an EAP is counselling, which is confidential and covers work-related and non-work-related problems. General feedback on the types and sources of employee stress at counselling sessions may be useful in identifying the primary causes of stress.

The EAP may be linked to the disciplinary procedure, insofar as discipline may be postponed if the employee agrees to join the EAP. In the event of the employee not agreeing to join the EAP, then the employer reserves the right to restart the disciplinary procedures.

The motivation behind EAPs may be pragmatic rather than philanthropic. EAPs may improve profitability through improved morale, increased productivity, reduced absenteeism, fewer industrial relations problems, staff turnover, medical and litigation costs. In addition, the image of the company is enhanced as organisations with EAPs are seen as caring employers.

Other corporate programmes

These include:

- **Health circles:** Health circles were developed in Germany in the late 1980s. Health circles are company problem-solving groups, modelled on quality circles. They have evolved to become a very successful tool in workplace health promotion. Like quality circles, the health circles focuses on short and medium-term improvement of working conditions and aspects of job design. They require a facilitator to guide the group through a problem-solving session. The health circle should have representatives from management, health and safety, occupational health, HRM, unions, and workers. There should be six to eight health circle meetings in total, each two to three weeks apart, during normal working time. Meetings should be governed by rules of fair discussion and minutes taken. Meetings focus on health-related issues and discussion of proposed solutions. The outcome should be to promote health, reduce work-related stress, and make employees responsible for their own health.
- **Child-care facilities:** Family-friendly policies such as flexitime and child-minding facilities can ease the pressures on families and single parents.
- **Flexitime** gives employees the opportunity to balance work and home commitments. Flexitime allows employees to set their own schedules within boundaries set by management. Workers may set their start and end times but must be at work within specified core times. The workweek may also be compressed into a shorter time frame – for example, four 10-hour days.
- **V-Time** (voluntary reduced time) is a system that allows full-time employees to reduce their working hours for a specified period with *pro rata* reduction in salary. It facilitates employees who want to spend more time with their families but differs from part-time work, in that it is a temporary arrangement with a return to full-time status guaranteed.
- **Sabbaticals** involve taking time off as paid or unpaid leave for up to 12 months to pursue some interest, with or without a guarantee of the same job on return to the organisation. Employees may use the opportunity for personal and career growth and development. It may also be used as a way to relieve job burn-out.

- **Career breaks** may be given to employees who want to pursue a full-time university degree or professional qualification. They are usually taken as unpaid leave with a guarantee of re-entry to the company on completion.
- **Teleworking** is where employees are allowed to work from home. With modern telecommunications technology, knowledge workers can operate from home almost as effectively as from the workplace. Advantages include savings on commuting time, savings in child minding fees, and more control over work pace. On the downside, teleworkers report that, when working from home, they feel isolated and lack social support.
- **Organisation development (OD):** OD interventions may be used to improve the structure of the organisation, the design of jobs and interpersonal relationships. Teamwork is one of the outcomes of such interventions.
- **Counselling:** Stress advisors with special training in stress counselling may be employed to provide one-to-one advice for stressed employees. Talking out problems to a sympathetic listener is still the best way of dealing with them. In the process, one may even get an insight into one's problems and how to handle them. Such advice should be supportive, enabling, empowering and confidential.
- **Mentoring and coaching:** A mentor is someone, other than your own boss, who will provide advice and support when you need it and help you find solutions to problems using the benefits of their wisdom and experience. The mobility of most people, the decline in social support systems and the lack of balance between home and work life, means there is an increasing need for corporate support systems such as mentoring and coaching. Coaching is where the manager gives instructions to staff to maintain or improve work performance. Research shows that those extensively mentored get more promotions, are more highly paid, and report higher job satisfaction than those who received little mentoring.
- **Social support** from work colleagues, supervisors, and managers should be encouraged and facilitated by the organisation. Social support is the extent to which employees feel they can trust each other, are interested in each other's welfare, respect one another, and have a genuine positive regard for each other. Employees need a sense of community to be happy in their work. *Work-based*

clubs and social outings could be encouraged and subsidised by the organisation to build up this level of trust and respect.

- **Role play:** Role play may be used to anticipate and rehearse approaches to conflict situations. Industrial relations, performance appraisal, and handling grievance and disciplinary procedures are just some of the potentially stressful occasions that can be prepared for using role play.

- **Information:** Employees should be kept informed about the financial, marketing and competitive status of the company. Some large companies run financial literacy programmes for their employees to help them understand the financial aspects of the business. Employees who are kept informed about the business affairs of the company feel they have a say in what is going on and more control over their lives. Employees are thus able to anticipate and adjust to upcoming changes and possibly given an opportunity to influence what is going to happen.

CORPORATE POLICIES

Corporate policies can have a major impact on stress at work.

Participation

Participation should be real, relevant, significant and supporting. 'Real' means not manipulative and illusory. 'Relevant' means that participation must refer to the particular work and needs of the employee. 'Significant' means that the participation should not be trivial and that management must support the participation.

There are two sides to participation. On the one hand, research indicates that participation improves the morale and performance of a workforce. On the other hand, some managers may resent a policy of participation and some employees may be reluctant to participate in anything.

Managers may hold the view that the prerogative of management is to manage. They may see participation as an erosion of their formal managerial role and powers. Thus participation may invoke feelings of resentment, loss, anger and anxiety. In practice, some managers may be unable or unwilling to adopt a participative style. Those who do may be subject to irreconcilable pressures of being participative and, at the same time, achieving high production and performance targets.

A participative style of management requires good interpersonal relationship skills. Managers from a technical or scientific background may give relationships a low priority, being more focused on getting the job done. Consequently, they may find interaction with other people a more stressful experience than those managers who are people-oriented.

Participation has been incorporated into employment legislation and become an employment standard in Norway, Sweden and Germany. An EU directive provides for worker directors and participation councils. Greater participation leads to lower staff turnover, higher productivity and less stress.

Downtime

Organisations should create opportunities for downtime or quiet time. People need time to recuperate and reflect. Employees can only improve work processes and procedures if they have time to think. This time is essential for continuous improvement, lifelong learning, and creativity.

Teamwork

The move to team-based organisations is resisted by some managers and supervisors, as they see it as a threat to their power and status. It is important that everything is done to bring these managers on board. A team-based organisation must have the support of all managers.

Employees need social and personal skills to function effectively in teams. Intra-personal skills training should be provided for them.

Managers and supervisors become facilitators rather than controllers. They need training for this new role. Team-building takes considerable effort and should be pursued systematically through training initiatives over a long period of time.

Empowerment

Empowerment means giving employees control and responsibility over their own work. It is the philosophy that everyone in the organisation should feel a sense of ownership and pride.

Empowerment liberates those with initiative. The more control these people have over their work lives, the less the degree of stress experienced. Others, such as those with an external focus of control, may find the experience distressful.

Dignity at work

Organisations should have a dignity at work policy in place. Workplaces should be caring, supportive environments, according dignity and respect to all workers. Cultures of harassment and bullying should not be tolerated. Employees should be praised for outstanding contributions and their value to the organisation acknowledged.

Monitoring stress

As a part of corporate policy, employees may be encouraged to use a stress diary to monitor their personal stress levels. This will enable them to consider and reflect on aspects of their work that they find stressful. Employees should consider each stressor, how they handled it, how it affected them, and how they can improve in the future. Stress diaries may provide source materials for topics of discussion at health circle meetings.

Stress audits may be taken by the company to identify potential sources of stress and to monitor employee health. A steering group may be set up to manage the process. Ideally, the group should consist of managers, employees, trade union representatives, and health and safety specialists.

The Occupational Stress Indicator (OSI) is widely used in the UK and some other countries to gather the relevant information and is said to be very reliable. It provides a wealth of information about how employees perceive the organisation and experience stress. The results may be analysed and benchmarked against similar organisations. Corrective action should be taken to eliminate the sources of stress. This may involve culture, policies, structure, job design and stress management programmes.

CORPORATE PROCEDURES

Corporate procedures can also impact on stress in the workplace.

Grievance

When a member of your staff alleges that the company, or a particular manager, has acted unfairly against them, you are dealing with a grievance. Examples include alleged discrimination, sexual harassment, unfair work distribution, bullying, and breaches of the employment contract.

Most organisations have a defined procedure for handling grievances. The grievance process can be both stressful for the manager and the employee. Because of this, most managers do not like dealing with grievances and prefer to procrastinate rather than nipping them in the bud. However, if they are ignored, they are likely to fester and develop into major industrial relations problems, thus creating major headaches for the future. In addition, the number of grievances in a particular department may indicate poor managerial styles and a stressful working environment.

Discipline

If an employee breaches a company rule, or consistently fails to reach the required level of job performance, then a disciplinary situation can arise. Examples of behaviour giving rise to disciplinary action include persistent lateness, absenteeism, dishonesty, alcohol or drug abuse, sub-standard job performance, refusal to obey a legitimate order, or unacceptable behaviour. In addition to company rules, the employee may be in breach of the employment contract or equality or health and safety legislation.

Most organisations have a defined procedure for handling disciplinary problems. Discipline is a very serious and stressful process for both the manager and the employee. The manager may have to make unpopular but necessary decisions, such as deductions from pay, stopping increments, demotion or even temporary or permanent suspension from work. The manager knows that the implications may be very serious for the employee, who may lose their only source of livelihood. There is also the fear that the employee will take an action in the courts for unfair dismissal. Most actions for unfair dismissal arise when the employee feels that he did not get a chance to defend himself. A high rate of disciplinary problems in a particular department may be symptomatic of a stressful working environment and poor management style.

Emails / Internet

An organisation should have a clear email/Internet policy in order to minimise its exposure to legal and other risks. The email policy adopted by the company should make it clear that email is solely for business use and that misuse may result in disciplinary action.

Misuse of email could expose a company to libel charges, breaches of equality legislation and copyright law. Recently, cases of employees downloading pornography, including child pornography, have been highlighted in the media. This abuse of company systems is in addition to the financial cost involved in staff wasting time on the irresponsible use of emails or the Internet.

The sending of explicit, suggestive or abusive emails to other employees may constitute sexual harassment or bullying. Disclosure of information on another employee via email may be in breach of data protection legislation.

Bullying

Bullying at work has been linked to employee ill-health, such as psychosomatic stress symptoms, musculo-skeletal symptoms, anxiety and depression. Ishmael and Alemoru (1999) define bullying as 'persistent, offensive, abusive, intimidating, malicious or insulting behaviour, which amounts to an abuse of power and makes the recipient feel upset, threatened, humiliated or vulnerable. Bullying undermines a target's self-confidence and may cause them to suffer stress'.

Bullying is the systematic and ongoing persecution of an individual that may cause severe social, psychological and psychosomatic problems for the victim. Bullying affects morale, creativity and initiative in the workplace. In extreme cases, bullying can result in distress, depression, nervous breakdown or even suicide.

Psychological bullying is more insidious than physical bullying, leaving no physical marks but causing more long-term damage. Psychological bullying includes sarcasm, teasing, verbal abuse, name-calling, back-biting, intimidation, scape-goating, manipulation, exclusion and isolation.

Einarsen (1999) reports that bullying can be categorised under five headings:
1. Work-related, including changing work tasks or making them difficult to perform.
2. Social isolation.
3. Personal attacks, such as ridicule, insulting remarks or gossip.
4. Verbal threats, such as criticism, shouting or humiliation in public.
5. Physical violence or threats of such violence.

Bullying can make a person's life a misery at work. Seigne *et al.* (1998) reports that 30 Irish victims of bullying described their workplace as a highly stressful, unfriendly and competitive place, plagued with interpersonal conflicts and managed through an authoritarian leadership style. The bully can be a manager, supervisor or fellow co-worker.

Bullying by a manager is seen as more stressful than that of a co-worker. Despite appearances, the bully is often an insecure individual, who uses bullying to assert their power and control over others. Autocratic styles of management can often be misconstrued as bullying. Managers often have to convey bad news to staff. Sometimes they lack the appropriate empathy skills and resort to bullying.

Bullying is now recognised as a major source of stress in the workplace and most organisations have policies in place to prevent it. *The policy should include clear and concise definitions of bullying, a statement that bullying is unacceptable and a disciplinary offence, and the procedures for resolving the issue.* It pays to do so as an organisation can suffer unwelcome adverse publicity and leave itself vulnerable to substantial damages in litigation cases or prosecution under health and safety legislation. The legal aspects of stress caused by bullying are dealt with in **Chapter 6**.

Confronting the bully

The victims of bullying can eliminate it by confronting the problem and bringing it to the attention of management if it persists. On the management side, the bully should be given an opportunity to rectify the problem by acquiring appropriate skills through training and development.

The skills identified as most likely to help with the problem of bullying include communication, conflict resolution, interpersonal relations, leadership, stress management and emotional intelligence. Emotional intelligence enables people to recognise their own emotions and others. The bully needs to exercise self-control over their emotions and learn how to empathise with others rather than resort to bullying.

Costigan (1998) highlights the following as the warning signs of bullying:

- Leaving employment before being offered another job.
- Sudden bouts of crying.
- Loss of appetite and/or sexual drive.
- Chain-smoking and/or uncharacteristic heavy drinking.
- Emotional withdrawal from family and friends.
- Difficulties in sleeping.
- Talking obsessively about work.

Sexual harassment

The European Commission Code of Practice on the Protection of the Dignity of Women and Men at Work (2000) defines sexual harassment as 'unwanted conduct of a sexual nature, or other conduct based on sex affecting the dignity of women and men at work. This can include unwelcome physical, verbal or non-verbal conduct'.

Sexual harassers are likely to be men in positions of authority over their victim – female sexual harassers are relatively rare. Supervisors are more likely to be the perpetrators of physical harassment rather than work colleagues.

Sexual harassment causes stress for the victim and lost productivity and high staff turnover for the company. Many cases have been successfully prosecuted through tribunals and the courts. *Every organisation should have a sexual harassment policy, including a system of help and advice, as well as disciplinary and legal remedies.*

Employees who are being sexually harassed should keep a detailed record of the harassment. This will be supporting proof that the sexual harassment has actually taken place.

If the harassment takes the form of sexual assault, then the victim can take an action under criminal law. *Organisations should have a code of practice for dealing with sexual harassment and should provide awareness training.* Assertiveness training can be very useful for developing skills for coping with sexual harassment.

Many cases of litigation against organisations have come before the courts because of sexual harassment. The legal aspects of stress caused by sexual harassment are dealt with in **Chapter 6**.

Discrimination

Race, religion, language, colour, gender, ageism, and socio-economic status are all potential sources of discrimination.

CORPORATE CULTURE

Organisational culture is the shared beliefs, values, and assumptions that guide a business in its dealings with others. It has been popularly described as 'the way we do business around here'. The culture is reflected in the structure, policies, logo, brands, and management style of the company. In addition, the culture is seen in how the company treats its employees and customers and how it presents itself to the outside world.

A workplace culture that encourages management not to see stress as a weakness should be encouraged. Managers should be trained to spot signs of serious job strain and deteriorating mental health, so that corrective action can be taken before they become problems.

Types of culture

Trompenaars (1993) classifies culture as:

- **Family:** This is a power-centred culture, where there is a strong emphasis on hierarchy and leadership. The leader may be viewed as a father figure who gives guidance and approval. This is usually found in small family businesses. However, some large organisations with a charismatic leader have a power culture. Employees are motivated by fear and punishment and loyalty and long service is highly valued. A leader with a Type A personality will make family cultures stressful to work in. It is difficult to change power cultures.
- **Eiffel tower:** This is a role-centred culture – for example, a typical bureaucracy with many management levels and clearly-defined roles. The guiding principles of a bureaucracy are logic, equity and efficiency. Authority depends on the position in the hierarchy and not on personal power. This type of organisation offers security, but it can be impersonal and frustrating to work in. It suits the employee who is happy to operate within defined systems and procedures. Those with initiative and creativity are likely to find the experience of working in a bureaucracy very stressful.
- **Guided missile:** This is a task-centred culture, where the emphasis is on getting the job done or meeting the needs of customers. Power depends on expertise, rather than position in the hierarchy. Tasks tend to exist within organisations in specific departments. Team-based projects are set up to deal with specific tasks. A task-centred culture may also be found in new start-up companies, particularly in new technology such as Internet companies. Task cultures tend to be high on getting the job done and low on consideration, and thus insensitive managers may cause stress for employees. Working in a project with tight deadlines can be exhausting and stressful; staff may suffer burnout, if a balanced approach to life is not adopted.
- **Incubator:** This culture emphasises the self-actualisation of the person. It is very concerned with the equality and dignity of the

person. In this type of culture, formality and structure are kept to a minimum. Professional partnerships such as doctors, dentists or lawyers often organise on this basis, sharing office space, equipment, secretarial services and so on. Community-based organisations and workers' co-operatives are other examples of this form. Since employees are encouraged to take responsibility for their own development, this type of organisation suits individuals who are independent-minded and self-motivated but it may prove stressful for those without initiative.

SUMMARY

Training interventions should cover interpersonal relations, self-management and general corporate programmes.

Job interventions can be recalled by the mnemonic REFRESH. This stands for:

- Rotation.
- Enrichment.
- Fit.
- Redesign.
- Enlargement.
- Sharing.
- HR Recruitment.

Corporate programmes include health promotion schemes, employee assistance programmes and counselling.

Corporate policies include participation, teamwork and empowerment.

Corporate procedures should be in place to handle grievance, discipline, email abuse, bullying, discrimination and sexual harassment.

Changing the corporate culture can be a difficult and long-term process. Culture types in companies include family, Eiffel tower, guided missile, and incubator. The 'family' is a power-centred culture. The 'Eiffel tower' is a role-centred culture. The 'guided missile' is a task-centred culture. The 'incubator' is a self-actualisation culture. Each culture creates its own unique stressors for employees.

10: PERSONAL STRESS INTERVENTIONS

- What are the psychological strategies for personal improvement?
- What is workaholism?
- What do we mean by balance?
- What is downshifting?
- What are the relaxation stress interventions?
- How can humour and laughter be used to reduce stress?
- What are the personal strategies for dealing with stress?
- What are the psychological coping strategies?

◆

What is this life if, full of care, we have no time to stand and stare?
WH Davies

MIND MAP OF CHAPTER 10

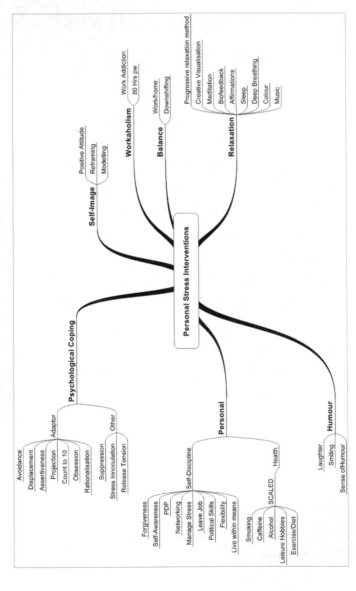

Having a positive attitude to life – seeing opportunities rather than problems – will lessen your stress levels. Workaholism is a major cause of burn-out. To avoid burn-out, we need to adopt a balanced lifestyle, making sure we leave time for personal, social and family needs. The appropriate use of relaxation techniques like creative visualisation, meditation, biofeedback and affirmations will counteract the stressors in your life.

Humour and laughter cost nothing and are some of the most effective antidotes to stress. Personal strategies such as creating personal development plans, adopting a healthy lifestyle, taking exercise, and developing an interesting hobby will also help you deal with stress in your life. Stress inoculation, assertiveness and avoidance are some of the psychological coping strategies for stress.

SELF-IMAGE

Positive attitude

A person's attitude can influence whether a situation or emotion is experienced as stressful. Positive thinkers see opportunities rather than problems. They see challenges rather than threats. On the other hand, negative thinking is seeing everything as a potential catastrophe. For example, if you like your job and find it interesting, you will see problems as challenges: problems thus become motivators. However, if you are unhappy with your job, you may see every little thing as an insurmountable problem: problems thus become stressors.

Reframing

Reframing is the ability to see things from a new perspective. If your boss is critical and domineering, reframe. Don't take it personally. Maybe the boss is insecure, or under pressure or has personal problems. This reframing will help you step outside yourself and see other possible reasons for the boss's behaviour, which will reduce the upset you are experiencing. For example, see mistakes and failures as learning opportunities and stress symptoms as the body's way of telling us to slow down.

The road to success is paved with failures. Bill Gates dropped out of Harvard University in 1975. He went on to found Microsoft Corporation and become the richest man in the world. Ronald Reagan lost the presidential race in 1968, and again in 1976. However, his persistence paid off when, in 1980, at 69 years of age, he became the oldest American to be elected President. Pope John Paul II, despite poor health, continues to persevere in carrying out his duties and is the most travelled Pope in history. Unlike these role models, the stress of failure puts an end to the ambitions of many people who are not as persistent, committed, and determined.

Modelling

Model your behaviour on people you know who are very good at handling stress. Study how they react to, and handle, specific stressors and model your behaviour on theirs.

British astrophysicist and Cambridge University mathematics professor Stephen Hawking has persevered through the pain and distress of a rare degenerative muscle disease. He is now the world's most famous mathematician, although confined to a wheelchair. Dr Viktor Frankl (1984), as he relates in his moving book, *Man's Search for Meaning*, was able to overcome the stress of being incarcerated in a concentration camp by the Nazis in the World War II, by positive thinking and setting goals to achieve – they were able to imprison his body but were unable to imprison his mind.

WORKAHOLISM

Do you work to live, or live to work?

Workaholics live to work. Just as people can get addicted to alcohol and drugs, people can also become addicted to work. Workaholism, or work addiction, is one of the main reasons for marriage breakdown and personal breakdown, such as burn-out. Work addiction is where you are obsessed with your work to such an extent that your whole identity and self-worth is tied up with your work. Work addiction has been linked to high blood pressure and heart disease.

The work addict may feel their behaviour is justified by the benefits received such as promotion, status, praise and an attractive reward package. It may also be encouraged by the culture of the company. However, because of their work addiction, they have no time to enjoy the benefits. There is nothing wrong with being a loyal, committed, hardworking and dedicated employee. It only becomes a problem when you become totally obsessed with your job and neglect your personal and family life.

Workaholics work anything up to 80 hours a week, continually work late, rarely take holidays, take work home with them, work week-ends, find it difficult to delegate, and talk about nothing else but their work. In the short-term, most people will be able to cope with this severe physical and mental strain. From time to time, most of us have put in extra effort and hours when the exigencies of the work situation demand it. However, in the long-term, this type of commitment is likely to result in complete physical and mental exhaustion.

Work addicts are different from people who work hard but find their work challenging. The person challenged by their work has a balanced lifestyle and keeps the job in perspective. He realises that there are more things in life besides work. Therefore, he sets aside time for family, friends, and recreational pursuits.

The work addict is driven by fear of failure or rejection. While the work addict works extremely hard, he is unlikely to be happy, productive or creative. He is highly critical of his own shortcomings and those of others. On the other hand, the challenged person, driven by the love, interest and enjoyment inherent in the job, is likely to be more productive and creative than the workaholic.

Balance

Thoughtful employees are now more interested in balancing work, play, study, community and family life than spending long hours at work to earn more money. Quality of life is now seen as a more important issue for many employees than wealth. Such individuals prefer shorter working hours, manageable workloads, job security, control over one's career, and time to enjoy family and recreational pursuits.

Workstress.net (Autumn 2002) reports that nearly half of British fathers barely see their children grow up because they work too hard. One in four work early mornings and more than twice as many regularly work in the evenings up to 8.30 pm. A recent study found that one in three fathers regularly breach the 48-hour limit set by the European Working Time Directive. Often, mothers also put in long hours at the expense of family life. People in professional jobs put the long hours down to their career aspirations and family needs. By contrast, working class parents are more likely to say that their employers give them no choice.

Balance is also needed during the course of the workday. Nobody would expect a footballer to play an entire game without taking a break. Yet many otherwise rational people work from dawn to dusk without taking periodic breaks, and then wonder why they are feeling stressed. In a work situation, employees need down-time or time for rest, recuperation, and reflection. The benefits include improved concentration with fewer mistakes and accidents.

Reflection will help you put things in perspective. People who work all the time have no time to reflect. To work without reflecting is like eating without digesting. It is during reflective time that people are most creative. Use this time to think over your mistakes; why you went wrong, and in the future, how to avoid such errors. Learn from your mistakes. Continuous improvement should be your aim.

The need for rest is now recognised under health and safety legislation requiring employers to provide specified rest periods.

Flexible working arrangements such as fixed term contracts, part-time work, or job sharing, go some way in meeting the needs of employees who want to combine work and family life. Many organisations have flexitime, giving employees choices about the time they start and finish work. Others offer compressed working weeks of 4 days of 10 hours each, so employees can work intensively for four days and have three days off each week to devote to their personal and family lives.

Employees who work in firms with family-friendly policies experience less job stress and more job satisfaction.

Downshifting

Downshifting is where a person decides to exchange work time and status for more leisure and free time.

Many people are realising that they can live simpler and cheaper and more fulfilling lifestyles. Do we really need all the possessions that a modern lifestyle dictates? For some, rejecting promotion, negotiating part-time work or family friendly hours may be the trend for the future. Others may opt for teleworking or freelancing. More people than ever are quitting the rat race, because climbing up the corporate ladder often makes them lose sight of the simple but important things in life, such as seeing their children grow up and being around to help them with their homework. They realise that the best gift you can give to your children is your time.

In reality, older people and single people often find it easier to downshift than married people or people with dependants. Professional employees often find it easier than others to set themselves up as self-employed and organise their work hours to suit their lifestyles. Information technology, email and the Internet have made it easier for people to work in this way.

Relaxation

Every now and then, go away, take a little relaxation, because when you come back to your work your judgement will be surer. To remain constantly at your work will cause you to lose power of judgement. Go some distance away, because then the work appears smaller and more of it can be taken in at a glance, and a lack of harmony or proportion is more readily seen.
Leonardo da Vinci

Personal interests and hobbies provide a natural antidote to stress. Simple things like sitting quietly, reading a book, listening to music, taking a walk or relaxing in a bath are all good ways of counteracting stress.

The following are some well-known methods of counteracting stress through relaxation (readers who want to explore these topics further should consult the many specialist books or audiotapes on the subject):

- **Progressive relaxation:** This method tenses and relaxes in turn all the muscles in the body from head to toe. Hold the muscles tense for a period of five seconds and relax them for another 10 seconds. Repeat the exercise 10 times for each major muscle group. It is easy to learn and apply. All you need is a quiet private place to practice the routine.
- **Creative visualisation:** This is a mental process where you establish a goal and then imagine the process of attaining that goal. The brain does not know the difference between a real and an imagined event. This is why, when we imagine a lemon, our saliva glands become active. You can visualise a favourite pleasant scene such as a running stream or the waves of the ocean lapping the shore. This may be a place that you go to in your mind to relax mentally. Thoughts are powerful: in a sense, you are what you think. Successful actors, athletes, and businesspeople use visualisation to achieve their goals.
- **Meditation:** Meditation has been practiced in the East for hundred of years and has now been adopted by the West as a method for counteracting stress. Meditation means sitting quietly and focusing your attention on one thing at a time such as your breath, a candle flame, a prayer or a mantra. Meditation is a type

of distraction, based on the principle that you can't meditate and worry at the same time. Meditation can bring you to a state of deep relaxation called the serenity zone, thus decreasing stress, anxiety and depression. There is increasing scientific evidence that meditation can lower blood pressure, heart rate, and calm breathing; in the long-term meditation can lower high blood pressure significantly. Meditation is best learnt on a formal training course.

- **Biofeedback** systems use electronic sensors to measure and feedback stress levels. It is based on the same principles that lie-detectors use: when you are under stress, you perspire more and so skin that is damp from perspiration conducts electricity more effectively than dry skin. Such devices help you to monitor and control stress levels.

- **Affirmations:** This is where you counter negative thoughts with positive affirmations. The subconscious mind believes what you constantly feed it. To be effective, affirmations should be positive, personal, and made in the present tense. You can use affirmations to build self-confidence and substitute positive behaviours for negative ones. Examples of affirmation are: 'I am in control of my life', 'I am relaxed, calm and confident', 'I reflect and learn valuable lessons from my mistakes', or 'I can achieve my goals'. Remember your affirmations must be realistic: no amount of positive affirmations will turn a five-foot man into a world-class basketball or rugby player.

- **Sleep:** Rapid eye movement (REM) sleep is a stage of sleep where you are actively dreaming – such sleep is necessary for a proper night's rest. Chronic sleep deprivation knocks years off your life, and will reduce your productivity and efficiency. Proper restful sleep is a simple and key remedy in reducing stress and helping you function better during the day.

- **Deep breathing:** Taking a deep breath before an important interview or presentation will reduce your stress level. Inhale deeply for five seconds and exhale for the same timeframe.

- **Colour:** Research shows that colours have a significant impact on feelings. Bright reds, oranges and yellows energise us, while greens and blues have a calming effect.

- **Listening to music:** An easy way to wind down is to take time off to listen to your favourite music. Listening to classical music is thought to be particularly relaxing. Baroque music is claimed to enhance the ability to learn.

HUMOUR & LAUGHTER

Humour is a type of reframing, as it changes the perception of events. A sense of humour helps us to see the incongruities of life and gives us a sense of perspective on our problems. We are less likely to feel depressed and helpless, if we can laugh at our troubles. We cannot control the events in our external world but we can control the way we perceive them and thus our emotional response to them.

Humour and laughter engages both the left-hand side and right-hand side of the brain. The left side is the analytical side, which processes words. The right side is the creative side of the brain. When we see the humour in situations, we engage both sides of the brain.

One humourist said: 'Don't take life too seriously as you'll never get out of it alive'. Learn to laugh at yourself. It is known that people with a good sense of humour recover quicker from illness than those without. Norman Cousins (1981), a highly influential writer, attributed his own recovery from an apparently incurable condition to the healing power of laughter.

During laughter, the heartbeat quickens and blood pressure rises. However, after laughter, our blood pressure and pulse rates drop slightly. Endorphins, painkilling hormones that give us a sense of well-being, are released, and stimulate our immune system so that our stress level is reduced. Laughter is the perfect antidote for stress.

PERSONAL STRATEGIES

Some personal strategies that you may find useful include:

Self-discipline

Self-discipline is a key personal strategy in combating stress. Use these techniques:

- **Forgiveness:** Forget past wrongs and resentments. Don't hold grudges. Let go of the past and move on with your life. Get rid of anger. You are more prone to heart attacks, if you bottle up resentment and anger.
- **Develop self-awareness:** Know your strengths and weaknesses. Know your limitations and when to seek help from others. Learn about the signs and symptoms of stress and the strategies you can adopt and implement to counteract them.

- **Personal development plans:** Some organisations encourage their employees to prepare personal development plans. Even if your employer does not, you should prepare one yourself. The personal development plan should identify your strengths and weaknesses and training and development needs, and it will help you to take responsibility for your own career. The plan will give purpose and direction to your career aspirations, ensuring that you are taking positive steps to achieve your career goals rather than waiting for others to act.

- **Network for social and emotional support:** A problem shared is a problem halved. Networking is particularly useful when you lose your job or retire. Network with an outside mentor or hire the services of a personal coach, who may help you complete a life audit.

- **Manage the stressful situation:** Anticipate and rehearse strategies to deal with potential stressors. The more control you feel you have over situations, the less stress you'll experience. Use the problem-solving and ABCDE approaches discussed in **Chapter 8**.

- **Leave the organisation:** In the final analysis, if you consider the work you are doing to be too stressful and a danger to your health, you should think about alternative employment. Ideally, you should only work in an organisation that has values in harmony with your own. However, in times of high unemployment, this may not be a viable option.

- **Develop political skills:** People with political skills are socially astute, with high emotional IQs. Social skills such as communication, facilitating, coordinating, coaching, and influencing are particularly critical for today's managers and executives.

- **Flexibility:** Einstein's definition of insanity was 'Doing the same thing again and expecting a different result'. If something you are doing does not create the desired outcome, then you should do something else. Repeating the same behaviour over and over again causes much stress, even though it is obvious that it is not working. Try different behaviours until you discover one that is more useful.

- **Live within your means:** In surveys, the number one source of stress reported is often worry over money matters. People who try to maintain lifestyles they can't afford are more likely to have health problems. Calvin Coolidge said 'There is no dignity quite so impressive and no independence quite so important as living within your means'.

Health

You can counteract work-related stress by looking after your health. Your health is your wealth.

The personal health strategies to counteract stress can be recalled by the mnemonic SCALED:

- **Smoking:** Give up smoking and cut down on drinking. Even passive smoking is now considered a danger to health. Cigarette-smoking is now the single most important preventable cause of illness and death. Those who stop smoking reduce their chances of heart disease and cancer.

- **Caffeine** stimulates the adrenal glands to produce two stress hormones – adrenalin and cortisol. In the short term, caffeine improves concentration and increases energy; however, in the long term, high levels of cortisol shrinks part of the brain responsible for memory, blunts the immune systems and thus interferes with the body's ability to fight infections. Thus cutting down on cups of coffee will reduce your stress levels, preserve your memory and improve your health. People who give up caffeine claim that they are more relaxed, sleep better, have more energy, less heartburn and fewer muscle aches.

- **Alcohol** in small amounts may be beneficial and help you relax – for example, a glass or two of wine a day is good for you as it makes your blood less sticky and thus you are less likely to suffer from blood clots or strokes. However, large amounts of alcohol will interfere with your sleep patterns and cause hangovers. Alcoholic drinks are high in calories and thus also contribute to obesity.

- **Leisure interests and hobbies:** Hobbies provide pleasure and diversion from work life. Hobbies should be completely different from your normal line of work, although sometimes a hobby may become a source of income. There is a 4,000-year-old inscription on an Assyrian tablet, which says 'The gods do not subtract from the allotted span of men's lives the hours spent in fishing'. Don't begrudge yourself time for recreation. It is unlikely that, on your deathbed, you will say that you should have spent more time in the office!

- **Exercise:** In addition to the obvious physical benefits of exercise, it improves cardiovascular condition, reduces stress, anxiety and depression and improves digestion and sleep. Exercise also increases the blood flow to the brain improving alertness, concentration and memory performance. Build some form of exercise into your daily routine.

- **Diet:** Avoid the three whites: White sugar, white bread and white salt. Eat a healthy varied diet including fresh vegetables, fruit, fish, nuts, meats, poultry, whole grain bread and cereals. Oily fish such as salmon, mackerel and sardines are particularly good choices, as they are rich in omega 3, essential fats that help to counteract the blood-thickening effects of adrenaline, which is produced when we are stressed. Similarly, dark chocolate is beneficial for your health because it contains high levels of catechins, which reduce cholesterol levels and keep arteries healthy.

Psychological coping

The main ways of coping psychologically can be recalled by the mnemonic ADAPTOR:

- **Avoidance and withdrawal:** Avoid stress by mentally and physically leaving the scene. People withdraw from the work situation by missing deadlines, through absenteeism, taking longer lunch breaks, tardiness, or in the final analysis, quitting their jobs. All of these situations are merely running away from problems rather than confronting the issues. However, avoidance may be useful in certain circumstances to avoid people or situations that are likely to be stressful.
- **Displacement:** Channel energy into action so that you do not have time to think about your real problems.
- **Assertiveness:** Assertiveness means being able to express your needs, preferences, and feelings in a way that is not offensive or threatening to others. Many people experience stress in their normal everyday lives because they lack assertion skills. For example, a person may jump ahead of them in the queue at the supermarket. Instead of asserting their rights, they may say nothing and just fume inside. This is a type of psychological self-abuse that erodes self-esteem and benefits neither party. Assertiveness is discussed in more detail in **Chapter 11**.
- **Projection** is where people fail to take responsibility for their own actions and blame everybody else. People with shortcomings often project their inadequacies on to others, when in fact they are really referring to themselves.
- **Ten:** When about to have negative outbursts, bite your lip or count to 10.

- **Obsessed with routine:** The extreme manifestation of this is in obsessive compulsive disorder (OCD), an illness which should be treated by a psychologist or psychiatrist. Perfectionism is a type of OCD.
- **Rationalisation:** This is a defence mechanism to conceal the true motivations for one's actions, thoughts, or feelings. We often invent excuses to justify actions that are contrary to our better instincts.

Other psychological coping methods are:
- **Suppression:** Suppression involves denial or the pretence that something that exists is not really there. We use alcohol to suppress fear and drugs to suppress sadness. Denial may be an effective defence mechanism in some instances, particularly in the early stages of trauma. For example, in the early stages of bereavement, most people deny that their loved one is dead. In the short-term, denial helps people cope with traumatic situations. In the long-term, denial may be self-defeating and prevent healthy coping and progress towards other stages of adjustment and recovery from stressful situations.
- **Stress inoculation:** This is a type of desensitisation by preparing mentally for a known stressful event in advance. Under this approach, you focus on worst case scenarios. By anticipating your worst fears, you can think through strategies for dealing with them. Thus you will manage the situation better when it actually happens, because you are mentally prepared for it. Stress inoculation theory suggests that the gradual introduction of change is likely to be more acceptable to employees than immediate implementation.
- **Release tension** on a punch bag or effigy.

SUMMARY

Developing a good self-image and self-confidence are strong antidotes to stress. Having a positive attitude and reframing or seeing things from a different perspective will often enable you to manage events successfully and stress-free.

Workaholism is where employees are so obsessed with their work that they have no time for anything else and so their family and health suffers.

Balancing means having appropriate time for work, rest, play, family, friends, and recreation. Downshifting is where a person decides to exchange work time, money and status for more leisure and free time.

Learn to relax by practising techniques like the progressive relaxation method. Listening to your favourite music is an easy and effective way to lower your stress level.

Humour and laughter will help you not to take life too seriously. It is hard to smile and feel unhappy at the same time.

Personal strategies such as developing outside interests, taking exercise, and living a healthy lifestyle will help you live a stress-free life.

The main psychological coping strategies can be recalled by the mnemonic ADAPTOR, which stands for:

- Avoidance.
- Displacement.
- Assertiveness.
- Projection.
- Ten – count to 10.
- Obsession.
- Rationalisation.

Stress inoculation suggests that you can get used to a potential stressful situation by gradual exposure to it, so that, when it actually happens, you are less likely to find the situation stressful.

11: Surviving Stress

- What are the key time management skills?
- How can I delegate more effectively?
- How can I be more assertive?
- What are the conflict resolution strategies?

◆

Know the true value of time; snatch, seize and enjoy every moment of it. No idleness, no laziness, no procrastination.
Lord Chesterfield

MIND MAP OF CHAPTER 11

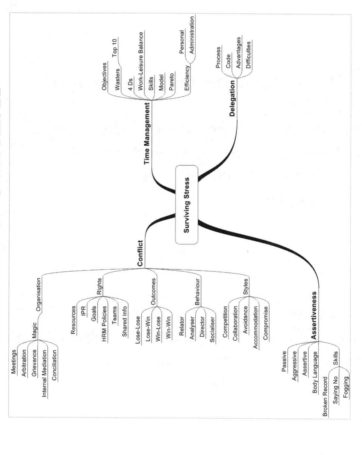

You can thrive on stress by implementing the appropriate personal and other intervention strategies discussed in previous chapters. In the work context, you can lessen your exposure to stress by developing time management, delegation, assertiveness, and conflict resolution skills. People are often stressed because they do not know how to organise their time effectively. Managers are often overworked because they fail to delegate work to subordinates.

People often take on too much work because they lack assertiveness and are thus reluctant to say 'No'. They thus take on more work than they can cope with.

Managers are sometime anxious and irritable because they do not know how to resolve conflicts in the workplace. Managers can equip themselves to handle conflict by practising the styles of conflict management.

TIME MANAGEMENT

Take the time to work, for it is the price of success.
Take the time to think; it is the source of strength.
Take the time to play; it is the secret of youth.
Take the time to read; it is the seed of wisdom.
Take the time to be friendly, for it brings happiness.
Take the time to dream; it will carry you to the stars.
Take the time to love; it is the joy of life.
Take the time to be content; it is the music of the soul.
Original Irish text – author unknown

There is the same number of hours in a day for all of us. You cannot borrow, steal, hoard or earn more time. You can only invest, spend, organise or waste time.

Managing time is called work study for workers, organisation and methods for administrators, and time management for managers. Irrespective of what it is called, it is all about managing your time efficiently and effectively – working smarter rather than harder.

Objectives of time management

The objectives of time management are to:

- Achieve our goals.
- Feel a sense of control.
- Reduce stress.

- Allocate time to important areas.
- Feel a sense of progress.
- Create balance in our lives.
- Reduce effort and be efficient.
- Enjoy life.
- Feel we have choice.

The top 10 time wasters are:
- Telephones: Plan your phone calls to avoid wasted time.
- People dropping in: Discourage casual callers.
- Poor planning.
- Procrastination and indecision: Procrastination – putting off until tomorrow what you should do today – is known as 'the thief of time'. Procrastination has been explored in **Chapter 2**.
- Unnecessary checking and correcting of others' mistakes. Get it right first time and save correction and checking time.
- Bureaucratic office procedures: simplify procedures and get rid of unnecessary paperwork.
- Problems with computers: Improve your computer literacy.
- Poor organisation structure: Change your organisation structure to empower people and use teams.
- Meetings: The time spent on any item on the agenda usually will be in inverse proportion to its value. So, you should have a time limit for the meeting with a specific time allocated for each item on the agenda. The purpose of the meeting should be clear and only those who need to be there should be invited. An agenda should be drawn up and minutes of the meeting taken. Proposed actions should be allocated to people and followed up for completion
- Emails: Allocate a specific time during the day for handling emails. Grouping work tasks is more efficient and saves time.

The four Ds of time management are:
- **Desire:** You must really want to become an expert at time management and to practice its principles.
- **Decision:** You must take an immediate decision to put the principles of time management into operation.
- **Determination:** The postage stamp sticks to only one thing until it gets there. You will need goals to guide you to your purpose and determination to keep you there.

- **Discipline:** Self-discipline is the ability to stick to a task and see it through to the end. It requires concentration and the willingness to forego immediate gratification for the achievement of a desired outcome in the future.

The time management model (**Figure 2**) will help you manage your time better.

FIGURE 2: THE TIME MANAGEMENT MODEL

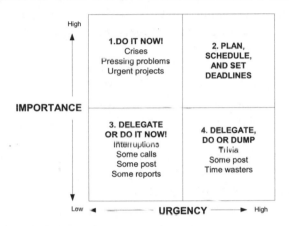

Box 1. Jobs that are important and urgent should be done immediately.

Box 2. Jobs of high importance but low urgency should be scheduled for a future date. These jobs will become urgent as the deadline approaches: this is the heart of time-management. Building relationships, strategic planning, preventive maintenance, and financial planning, if provided for and acted on, will reduce the number of items in Box 1.

Box 3. Jobs of low importance but which are urgent should be delegated or done immediately.

Box 4. Jobs of low importance and low urgency should be delegated or dumped. Next to the dog, the waste paper basket is a man's best friend. You should try and keep out of Boxes 3 and 4 because urgent or not, they are not important.

Key time management skills include:
- Dealing with others: Control uninvited callers and unpredictable interruptions that consume time.
- Keep a time diary to identify how you spend your time.
- Planning and scheduling: Plan your work and work your plan.

- Responding effectively in a crisis: Contingency plans will help you do this.
- Finishing things: Deal with one thing at a time. Multi-tasking may be popular, but prioritising and concentrating on one thing at a time is more efficient and more effective.
- Evaluating options objectively: Use a cost/benefit analysis approach where appropriate.
- Motivating yourself by setting objectives and deadlines.
- Seeing better ways to do work: Formal training in method study and creativity will help you here. Aim for continuous improvement through lifelong learning.
- Getting resources to help.
- Delegating: Train your staff so they are able and willing to do the delegated tasks.
- Allowing for contingencies or the unpredictable things that can happen each day such as interruptions and emergencies.

The Pareto principle is also known as the law of the critical few and the trivial many: 20% of what you do accounts for 80% of your results. Therefore, 80% of your time may be spent on unproductive and unprofitable activities. Results come from doing the right thing, not doing things right. You must be effective as well as being efficient.

Key result areas should be your number one priority. The 'nice to do' jobs should be candidates for elimination.

Aim to be efficient in your use of time:

PERSONAL EFFICIENCY

- **Waiting time:** Use queuing, travel and commuting time as self-improvement time. Learn while you wait. Some people attend a 'mobile university', by listening to educational tapes as they commute.
- **Communication skills:** Develop good communication skills. Good verbal and written communication skills are essential requirements for any manager.
- **Listening skills:** Develop good listening skills. Listen carefully to get the facts. You should listen twice as much as you speak.
- **Develop speed-reading skills:** The average person reads up to 300,000 words per week. As a manager, it may pay you to do a speed-reading course – and to become more selective in what you read.

- **Memory skills:** Do a memory-training course to develop powers of greater concentration and retention. Practice memory techniques, such as mind maps, mnemonics, coding systems, and visualisation.

ADMINISTRATIVE EFFICIENCY

- **Prepare a 'to do' list:** Prioritise the list into three categories A, B and C, A being 'must do', B being 'should do' and C being 'nice to do'. Estimate how long the A and B items should take. Review jobs that have taken longer to discover the reasons why
- **Organise your desk:** Remove distractions – you should only have that on which you are working in front of you. Do one thing at a time. Get finished jobs out of the way. Create a 'slush' file for grey areas.
- **Plan your phone calls:** Decide in advance how long the phone call should take. Stick to your time budget. Screen incoming calls. Batch your calls for certain quiet periods of the day and do them altogether. Use voice mail to batch incoming calls, as appropriate.
- **Stick to an appointment procedure:** This will help you to plan and control your day.
- **Prioritise:** Draw up a priority list for each day and stick to it. Cross off the jobs you complete as you go along.

DELEGATION

Delegation is the process of assigning responsibility to an individual or group to carry out a particular task or action. It means, in effect, that the manager entrusts part of his work to team members.

Management has been defined as getting work done through other people. Therefore, to manage effectively, a manager must delegate. In practice, this is quite difficult to do. Managers like doing the work that brought them their first promotion from operational duties to a management role. However, the manager must recognise the role change from performing tasks to managing others. Their job is now to concentrate on their managerial role of planning, leading, organising, motivating, delegating and controlling. To achieve this, they must move away from their operational role and adopt a managerial role.

Delegation does not mean an abdication of responsibility. The manager or supervisor is still responsible for the work of the section. You can delegate authority but you cannot delegate responsibility. However, by delegating, the manager empowers the staff and makes them accountable to him for the correct performance of the work delegated.

Delegation process

The delegation process consists of the following stages:

- The manager assigns duties and tasks to the staff for completion to a defined standard of performance.
- The manager gives the staff sufficient authority to perform the tasks delegated but retains ultimate responsibility. The authority should be clearly defined.
- The manager makes the staff accountable to him for the correct performance of the tasks delegated.
- The manager lets the staff get on with the job without undue interference. Initially, some guidance and coaching may be necessary. In time, an occasional check on progress should be sufficient. Never tell people how to do things. Tell them what to do and they will surprise you with their ingenuity.

Delegation – a code of good practice

A code of good practice should cover the following:

- The manager should set clear objectives and sub-objectives.
- Performance standards of quantity, quality, cost and time should be set.
- The manager should provide the staff with sufficient authority and resources to get the job done. It is a prerequisite that the staff must be willing, able and have the appropriate skills and experience to do the tasks delegated.
- Depending on the experience of the staff, facilitation rather than control should be the objective. Nevertheless the progress of the work should be monitored against sub-objectives.
- The manager should ensure that the staff are sufficiently experienced or trained to do the work.
- The manager should ensure that the task is completed to the standards of performance agreed.
- Only appropriate tasks should be delegated. Certain tasks such as discipline, performance appraisal, rewards, praise and reprimand, and tasks requiring the status of the managerial role, are the prerogative of the manager and must not be delegated.

Advantages of delegation

The advantages of delegation include:

- It frees the manager to concentrate on the duties for which he is primarily employed – to manage others.
- Delegation is a great way to empower, train and develop staff. Work that the manager finds routine may offer considerable challenge and opportunities for development to staff.
- Job enrichment and job enlargement are achieved mainly through delegation and are a great way of motivating staff through improved responsibility and job satisfaction.
- Delegating challenging work may be a method of recognition and reward for staff with outstanding on-the-job performance.

Difficulties of delegation

The following are some of the reasons why some managers find it difficult to delegate:

- There is always the fear that the work will not be done satisfactorily. The manager may feel vulnerable, as he is ultimately responsible for the work delegated.
- Some tasks are vocational hobbies with managers. They made their name and earned their reputations and first promotion by doing this type of work and are thus reluctant to give it to somebody else.
- Some managers like to look busy all the time This prevents them from doing the difficult task of thinking What better way to achieve this than by doing routine tasks? They don't realise that thinking and reflection are very important aspects of management.
- The process of delegation and instruction may be slow and time-consuming and the manager often feels that he would be quicker doing the task himself. However, the investment in time and effort is a once-off and will be more than compensated by the time saved in the long-term.
- Some managers believe that nobody can do the job as well as they can. They like to feel on top of every job detail and the only way they can achieve this is by doing everything themselves.
- Some managers feel insecure and threatened by up-and-coming ambitious staff. They may feel the success of their staff and the recognition they get would be a threat to them rather than a compliment to their managerial and staff development skills.

- Some managers may lack confidence and trust in their staff. Handy (1985) expressed this by the equation $T + C = Y$ where T equals trust, C equals control and Y is a constant – Handy described this as the 'trust / control dilemma'. The more trust you have in your staff, the more you will delegate and the less you will control. The less trust you have in your staff, the less you will delegate and the more you will control. How much to delegate is therefore a managerial dilemma.

ASSERTIVENESS

Many managers take on more work than they can handle because they are unable to say the simple word 'No'. Tactfulness and straight talking are the keys to being assertive without causing offence. Understanding the difference between being passive, aggressive and assertive will help you develop assertiveness skills.

The passive person becomes a doormat, letting people walk all over them. They have difficulty standing up for themselves and often invite persecution by adopting the role of victim or martyr. They never express their true feelings or assert their rights. They suppress their upset and resentment about the situation and let it develop as if nothing is wrong. The third party is unaware of their feelings because they have failed to express them. The passive person fails to achieve their goals and, in the process, evokes pity or scorn rather than respect. Passive and aggressive behaviour both stem from low self-esteem.

The aggressive person asserts their rights but in a way that upsets or humiliates others. Aggressiveness implies lack of respect for other people's wants and needs, as it seeks to impose one's own opinions. When your anger subsides, you are likely to feel embarrassed as you recognise that you over-reacted to the situation. In the short-term, you may have got what you wanted but, in the long-term, you have created enemies. The aggressive person always assumes the worst motives for the other person's behaviour and counter-attacks. Inevitably, the aggressive person evokes resentment.

The assertive person asserts their rights in a tactful, but firm, manner, without causing offence to others. It is direct, honest communication between individuals interacting equally and taking responsibility for themselves. Assertive people know how to express their feelings and beliefs, ask for favours, give and receive compliments, and refuse unreasonable requests. The assertive person achieves their goals and earns respect in the process. If an assertive person is unsure why another person is behaving in an unreasonable way, they will ask questions to find out why. On the other hand, the passive person is afraid of being intrusive and therefore will shy away from asking questions.

Assertiveness means:

- Respecting yourself and other people.
- Taking responsibility for your actions but declining responsibility for other's problems.
- Recognising your needs and the needs of others.
- Asking for what you want.
- Express your feelings and give your opinions.
- Allowing yourself to make mistakes but at the same time enjoying your successes.
- Making clear 'I' statements to show you own and take responsibility for your feelings, opinions and thoughts.
- Changing your mind.
- Asking for time to think over the matter. Reflecting on issues – even overnight – can save you from jumping to conclusions.
- Dealing with others without being dependent on them for approval.
- Handling aggression with assertion.

There is often a double standard in operation about assertiveness: men who are assertive are seen as strong and dynamic, while women who are assertive are often seen as aggressive.

Body language

You use verbal and non-verbal communication to get your message across. It is important:

- To understand how the two interact, since body language reflects the unconscious and may give you away.
- That verbal and non-verbal communication support each other and that one does not contradict the other.

Your real feelings are mirrored by your tone of voice, gestures, posture, and eye contact. These are taken more seriously than your actual words, if the two are not in harmony with each other. Therefore, it is important that your assertiveness is accompanied by the appropriate body language, as follows:

- Look the person straight in the eye.

- Keep your body upright and your shoulders relaxed.
- Breathe normally.
- Smile as appropriate.
- Speak in a normal conversational tone.

Basic assertiveness skills

There are many assertiveness techniques available. The following are three of the most popular:

1. **'Broken record':** This is one of the most widely-used assertiveness techniques. It is called the 'broken record' because, when a record gets stuck, it plays the same thing over and over again. Similarly, you say the same thing over and over again until your message gets home or your wishes have been conceded. This technique will enable you to stand your ground when confronted with bullying or manipulation. It will also help you deal with authority figures in a confident and assertive manner.
2. **Saying 'No':** Many people find it very difficult to say 'No'. Some people find it difficult to say 'No' to those in authority; others may be afraid of the aggressive response that a 'No' might elicit. Remember that you have a right to say 'No' and that saying 'No' is much better than agreeing to something and subsequently leaving people down.
3. **'Fogging':** 'Fogging' allows you to be criticised without becoming defensive, anxious or argumentative while, at the same time, preventing the other person manipulating you. When someone is aggressive, they expect disagreement and charge right ahead without listening. Fogging slows them down with an unexpected 'Yes' response. You sidestep the issue, while still retaining your point of view, by partly agreeing with what they say – for example, if the boss says, 'That was a foolish proposal you put forward at the meeting', you might say, 'Yes, I can see that you think my proposal was foolish'. You are not agreeing with your boss; you are only saying that you can see that they believe that. Fogging will help calm things down rather than aggressively retorting and inflaming the situation.

CONFLICT RESOLUTION

Conflict is a fact of life. People disagree with each other for all sorts of reasons. Sometimes this disagreement results in anger, hostility and distrust. Conflict is a common source of stress.

In organisations, the main causes of conflict are the competition for jobs, promotion, resources, power and security. A significant proportion of a manager's time is consumed in trying to resolve conflict. People are genetically wired for 'fight or flight'. Fight results in conflict and hostility, whereas flight results in withdrawal or avoidance.

Not all conflict is bad. Conflict can be positive and constructive or it can be negative and destructive. A certain amount of conflict is good, in that it brings things out into the open, can lead to a cross fertilisation of ideas and an acceptance of alternative viewpoints. Other conflict is bad and may result in the breakdown of communications between individuals and between management and unions.

Styles of conflict management

There are five styles of conflict management (see **Figure 3**):

1. **Competition:** This is a win-lose style of management. Managers with this style use their formal authority, power, threats and coercion to get their way. Their behaviour is assertive and unco-operative. Competition without rules leads to conflict, as each side pursues their own incompatible goals.
2. **Collaboration:** This is a win-win style of management. Goals are compatible, with both sides engaging in mutual problem-solving. This style of management emphasises openness, trust, spontaneity and genuineness. Behaviour is both assertive and co-operative. Differences are clarified and the full range of alternatives to resolve the issue is considered before a meeting of minds is arrived at.
3. **Avoidance:** This is a style of management that tries to sweep the problem under the carpet. It is a type of withdrawal and suppression. It is merely a short-term solution, as the problem is likely to fester and arise again in the future, when it will be more urgent, critical – and difficult – to resolve.
4. **Accommodation:** This is a type of appeasement, where common goals are stressed and differences played down. It is altruistic to the extent that one party puts the other party's interest first. The style is unassertive but co-operative.

5. **Compromise:** This style of management tries to identify the middle ground. There is an element of give-and-take on both sides. If one party gives ground on a particular issue, the other yields something of equivalent value in return. Goals are neither completely compatible nor incompatible. Managers often use this style when engaged in industrial relations disputes with unions.

FIGURE 3: THE TWO-DIMENSIONAL MODEL OF CONFLICT MANAGEMENT

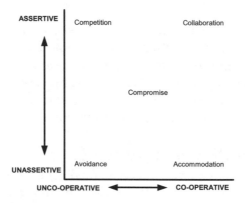

Source: McKenna, 2000.

Four basic behavioural styles

There are four basic behavioural styles (see **Figure 4**). Although no single behavioural style works better than another, the flexibility to get along with people with different styles than your own is a critical success factor when dealing with others.

The mnemonic RADS will help you recall the four styles:

1. **Relater:** Individuals with this style empathise with the needs of others. They value relationships with others and are reluctant to get directly involved in conflicts. They feel uncomfortable with, and resent, solutions that do not take the human element into account and thus may contribute to conflict in the organisation.

2. **Analyser:** Individuals with this style are more interested in logic and facts than relationships. They are conservative, uncomfortable with innovation and change and thus often a source of conflict in the organisation. They tend to be formal in their dealings with others and are slow to compromise in conflict situations.

3. **Director:** Individuals with this style are very assertive and poor at relationships. They are task-oriented and driven by objectives. They are risk-takers and are valued for their ability to get things done. They are confident, competitive and decisive and always leave no doubt as to whom is in charge. Because directors appear to be more interested in results rather than people, they appear cold, indifferent and autocratic thus sometimes causing resentment and conflict in an organisation.

4. **Socialiser:** Individuals with this style like being involved with other people. They have a high social or emotional intelligence. They tend to be creative and innovative and like to discuss their ideas with others. They have the ability to motivate and inspire others with their charm and vision of the future. On the other hand, their ideas may make other people uncomfortable and thus add to conflict in the organisation.

FIGURE 4: THE FOUR BEHAVIOURAL STYLES

ANALYSER	DIRECTOR
Logical	Independent
Thorough	Candid
Serious	Decisive
Systematic	Pragmatic
Critical	Determined
Precise	Efficient
Prudent	Objective
RELATER	**SOCIALISER**
Cooperative	Imaginative
Loyal	Friendly
Supportive	Enthusiastic
Diplomatic	Outgoing
Patient	Excitable
Easygoing	Persuasive
Respectful	Spontaneous

Source: Darling and Walker, 2001.

Conflict outcomes

There are four basic conflict outcomes (see **Figure 5**):

1. **Lose-lose:** This is where both parties to the conflict lose. Each side sees the problem only from its point of view and thus fails to analyse the problem in terms of mutual needs. They may arrive at an unsatisfactory compromise, which will only prove to be a short-term solution.

2. **Lose-win:** This is where one person sees the benefits of being defeated on the issue – 'losing the battle to win the war'. They see that it is better to sacrifice immediate gain for long-term advantage.

3. **Win-lose:** This is where one side wins a victory and the other side is defeated. This is often the situation in fierce competition or personal emotional conflicts. A manager may exercise wishes through personal power so that the employee has no say in the matter. The loser feels angry, bitter and vindictive and is only waiting for the opportunity to get even. It is only a short-term solution.

4. **Win-win:** The win-win strategy focuses on problem-solving and establishing common goals – which cannot be attained without cooperation. This is a creative solution, with both sides happy with the outcome.

FIGURE 5: THE FOUR OUTCOMES OF CONFLICT

		I want you to:	
		Lose	Win
I want you to:	Lose	**LOSE – LOSE**	**LOSE – WIN**
	Win	**WIN – LOSE**	**WIN – WIN**

Source: Davis and Newstrom, 1985.

Conflict resolution in organisations

There are many well-known formal methods for resolving conflicts in organisations. The key methods can be recalled by the mnemonic MAGIC:

- **Meetings:** These may be interdepartmental or team meetings. A chairman may be appointed to resolve differences between departments, which usually arise over issues of territory, power and status. Regular team meetings are an important way to avoid conflict between members of the team. Team members can clarify objectives, identify points of disagreement and solve problems before they degenerate into conflict.

- **Arbitration:** This is where a third party adjudicates on a dispute. The adjudicator hears the arguments of both sides, examines the evidence, and then makes a decision that may be favourable to one party and not to the other. This is very much a matter of last resort, as the parties agree to comply with the judgement.

- **Grievance:** The grievance procedure is a formal process within an organisation to solve employees' grievances. The employee may be accompanied by a work colleagues or trade union official when meeting with the manager. If the issue is not resolved, it may proceed up the management chain until resolution is achieved.
- **Internal or external mediation:** This is where a broker or peacemaker is appointed to resolve issues between disputing parties. Initially, each side is seen independently to establish the reasons for the disagreement and to provide a basis for returning to the negotiating table. Mediators sometimes put forward specific proposals for the parties to agree on. However, the final agreement is up to the parties themselves.
- **Conciliation and negotiation:** The parties get together to negotiate their differences under an independent chairman. They hope to resolve the issues involved.

Other strategies for resolving conflict in organisations can be recalled by the mnemonic RIGHTS:

- **Resources:** Competition for scarce resources causes conflict. A major source of conflict in organisations is the allocation of budgetary resources between departments. Policies should be in place to make sure that resources are allocated on an equitable basis. Conflict arises where people or departments feel they have been treated unfairly in relation to others.
- **Interpersonal relationships:** Differences between individuals and groups are often caused by personality clashes. Emotional IQ is needed to get along with other people. Some people are naturally good at getting along with others, while more need help and training in interpersonal relations, communication and problem-solving.
- **Goals:** A major source of conflict in organisations is a lack of goal congruence between management and staff. Each side is often pursuing different, and almost irreconcilable, goals. It is the responsibility of management to make sure that all the employees in the company are switched on to the same overall corporate objectives. A focus on vision, mission statements and clarification of strategic goals will help to achieve this aim.

- **HRM policies:** Equitable personnel policies will minimise and deal with the sources of conflict in an organisation. Fair selection systems, good reward systems, flexible-working arrangements, family-friendly polices, and training and development will help smooth the way.
- **Teams:** It is essential that the right people are selected for teams and that they go through a team-building process. Team-building takes time and patience and will not be achieved overnight. The boundaries between different teams should be co-ordinated and managed carefully so that inter-group conflict is avoided.
- **Shared information:** A participative style of management, with open communication, helps employees to know what is going on in the business. Disputes may be caused by misinformation and rumour. Employees like to have a broad knowledge of how the business is going and a detailed knowledge of issues affecting their immediate work.

SUMMARY

Time costs money and is our most precious resource. There is the same number of hours in a day for everybody. It is the way that you manage your time that matters: rather than counting time, you should make time count. The basic objective of time management is to work smarter not harder.

The four Ds of time management are desire, decision, determination and discipline. Having a work/leisure balance will lead to a productive and healthy life. Time management skills include keeping a diary, planning, scheduling and delegating.

The time management model indicates how to prioritise your time. The Pareto principle shows that 20% of your work activities achieve 80% of the results, which means that you should concentrate on the key result areas.

Personal and administrative efficiency are key elements of time management.

Delegation is the process of assigning responsibility to others to carry out a task or action. Many managers have too much work to do and experience considerable stress because they are either unwilling or unable to delegate. The good manager will know how to delegate in an effective way.

The advantages of delegation include freeing the manager from unnecessary routine and giving employees an opportunity for developing themselves. Difficulties include fearing that the employee will make mistakes and that the manager will be held responsible.

The unassertive manager is unable to say 'No' and so takes on more work than they can handle. Knowing the difference between passive, aggressive and assertive behaviour is important, if the manager wants to learn how to become more assertive. When assertive, your verbal and non-verbal communication should be in harmony. Key assertiveness skills include the broken record technique, the ability to say 'No', and the fogging technique.

The styles of conflict management are competition, collaboration, avoidance, accommodation and compromise. The four behavioural styles are relater, analyser, director, and socialiser. The four outcomes of conflict are lose-lose, lose-win, win-lose, and win-win. Well-known methods of managing conflict can be recalled by the mnemonic MAGIC, which stands for meetings, arbitration, grievance, internal mediation, and consultation. Other strategies for resolving conflict can be recalled by the mnemonic RIGHTS, which stands for resources, interpersonal relations, goals, HRM, teams and shared information.

BIBLIOGRAPHY

Balfour, Susan (2002). *Release Your Stress*, Hodder & Stoughton: London.

Costigan, Lucy (1998). *Bullying and Harassment in the Workplace*, The Columba Press: Dublin.

Cousins, Norman (1981). *Anatomy of an Illness as Perceived by the Patient: Reflections on Healing and Regeneration*, Bantam: New York.

Darling, John R. & Walker, W. Earl (2001). Effective conflict management: Use of the behavioural style model, *Leadership & Organisational Development Journal*, Vol.22, No.5, pp.230-242.

Davis, Keith & Newstrom, John W. (1985*). Human Behaviour at Work: Organisational Behaviour*, McGraw-Hill: New York.

Earnshaw, Jill & Morrison, Lynne (2001). Should employees worry? Workplace stress claims following the John Walker decision, *Personnel Review*, Vol.30, No.4, pp.468-487.

Einarsen, Stale (1999). The nature and causes of bullying at work, *International Journal of Manpower*, Vol.20, No.1, pp.16-27.

European Commission (2000). Code of Practice on the Protection of the Dignity of Women and Men at Work, European Commission: Brussels.

Frankl, Viktor, E. (1985). *Man's Search for Meaning*, Pocket Books, Simon & Schuster: New York.

Friedman, M. & Rosenman, R.H. (1974). *Type A Behavior and Your Heart*. Knopf: New York.

Handy, Charles (1985). *Understanding Organisations*, Penguin: London.

Harris, T.A. (1969). *I'm Okay – You're Okay: A Practical Guide to Transactional Analysis*, Harper & Row: New York.

Holmes, T.H. & Rahe, R.H. (1967). The social readjustment rating scale, *Psychosomatic Medicine*, Vol.11, pp.213-218.

Ismael, Angela & Alemoru, Bunmi (1999). *Harassment, Bullying and Violence at Work*, The Industrial Society: London.

Jinks, Annette & Daniels, Ruth (1999). Workplace health concerns: a focus group study, *Journal of Management in Medicine*, Vol.13, No.2, pp.95-105.

Liston-Smith, Jennifer (2001). Information Overload, Report from a Masterclass at the *CIPD HRD Conference*, 3-5 April 2001, Stress News, July, Vol.13, No.3.

McKenna, Eugene (2000). *Business Psychology and Organisational Behaviour*, Third Edition, Psychology Press Ltd: Hove, East Sussex.

Reuters Business Information (1996). *Dying for Information? An Investigation into the Effects of Information Overload in the UK and Worldwide*, Reuters: London.

Seigne, E., Rayner, C., Sheehan, M., and Barker, M. (1998). Bullying at work in Ireland, Bullying at Work, *Research Update Conference Proceedings*, Staffordshire University: Staffordshire.

Selye, Hans (1984). *The Stress of Life*, Revised edition, McGraw-Hill: New York.

Super, Donald (1957). *The Psychology of Careers*, Harper & Row: New York.

Trompenaars, F. (1993). *Riding the Waves of Culture*, Irwin: Chicago.

Further Reading

Atkinson, Jacqueline, M. (1988). *Coping with Stress at Work*, Thorsons: London.

Cartwright, Susan & Cooper, Cary L. (1997). *Managing Workplace Stress*, SAGE Publications: London.

Earnshaw, Jill & Cooper, Cary L. (2001). *Stress and Employer Liability*, second edition, CIPD: London.

Gillen, Terry (1997). *Assertiveness*, Institute of Personnel and Development: London.

Hanson, Dr. Peter (1988). *The Job of Stress*, Pan Books Ltd: London.

Hanson, Dr. Peter (1990). *Stress for Success*, Pan Books Ltd: London.

Harris, Clare (2003). *Minimise Stress, Maximise Success: How To Rise Above It All and Realise Your Goals*, Duncan Baird Publishers: London.

Humphreys, Tony (2000). *Work and Worth: Take Back Your Life*, Gill & Macmillan Ltd: Dublin.

Jones, Dr. Hilary (1997). *I'm Too Busy To Be Stressed, How to Recognise and Relieve the Symptoms of Stress*, Hodder & Stoughton: London.

Neenan, Michael (1993). Rational-Emotive Therapy at Work, *Stress News*, June, Vol.5. No.1.

Norfolk, Donald (1986). *Executive Stress: How to Recognise Stress and Make It Work for You*, Arrow Books Ltd: London.

Pettinger, Richard (2002). *Stress Management*, Capstone Publishing: Oxford.

Rice, Phillip L, (1999). *Stress and Health*, Third Edition, Brooks/Cole Publishing Company: Pacific Grove CA.

Useful Internet Sites

http://onlinestressnews.bizland.com/news.htm

http://www.ananova.com

http://www.isma.org.uk

http://www.jobstresshelp.com/news.htm

http://www.managingstress.com/articles/CBC.htm

http://www.stress.org/job.htm

http://www.stress-help.co.uk

http://www.vhihealthe.com

http://www.workstress.net

INDEX

ABOUT THE AUTHOR

Samuel A Malone is a self-employed training consultant and author. He is the author of six other books, including *Success Skills for Managers* and *Learning Skills for Managers* (both published by Oak Tree Press), as well as *Learning about Learning* (CIPD, 2003) and *How to Set Up & Manage a Corporate Learning Centre* (Gower, 2003). He runs a variety of training programmes and workshops on management, supervisory management and lifelong learning. He can be contacted at samalone@eircom.net.